Thoughts and Reflections on the Use of Magnesium

Thoughts and Reflections on the Use of Magnesium

Edited by

Gareth B. Neighbour and Ilias Oraifige
School of Engineering and the Built Environment,
Birmingham City University, Birmingham, UK.

Printed by Belmont Press

Published by:

The proceedings of the meeting on 'Thoughts and Reflections on the Use of Magnesium' held 20th July 2017 at Birmingham City University, United Kingdom, and run under the auspices of the Institute for Sustainable Futures.

Special Publication

ISBN: 978-1-904839-90-3

A Catalogue record for this book is available from the British Library

First printed in 2017 by Belmont Press

Published by Birmingham City University, Curzon Street, Birmingham, B4 7XG.

Printed in the United Kingdom

Foreword[1]

It is nearly half the weight of aluminium, 100% recyclable and the eighth-most abundant element in the earth's crust – so why don't we use magnesium more? Hoping to answer this question and increase the material's industrial reach, Birmingham City University (BCU), UK, has formed a strategic alliance with the world's largest producer of magnesium components, Meridian Lightweight Technologies. This book is one of the many outputs of the partnership.

Misconceptions of magnesium in the industry are still rife. A lot of people still believe it sets on fire easily. It doesn't, but the myth still dictates most people's present understanding, including engineers. However, while magnesium is not the simplest material to extinguish when alight – it continues to burn in nitrogen, carbon dioxide and water – its thermal conductivity makes it difficult to ignite in the first place. Magnesium is one of the best metals in terms of flammability, because it dissipates heat across its body so well, whereas steel, for example, localises the heat, so it can get very hot much more easily.

Attitudes towards magnesium aside, the partnership also aims to overcome technical challenges relating to high-pressure die casting (HPDC), particularly in making the process more applicable to low-volume components. The partnership is trying to see what can be done to allow small volume companies like Aston Martin, Lotus, Bentley and Rolls-Royce access and use magnesium. Aerospace, too, is a relatively low-volume industry. Difficulties in manufacturing relatively small product runs using HPDC stem from the up-front costs involved in equipment and tooling manufacture, complex tool and die setup involving multiple runners, and lengthy die changeovers.

The partnership is as much about adapting technical strategies as making engineering designers aware of the benefits of magnesium in components for which they would typically turn to aluminium. Aluminium alloys cannot be manufactured in as thin a wall stock as magnesium, as it doesn't flow as well through the mould during the HPDC process. This also means the expensive dies and tooling deteriorate far more quickly with aluminium. Rather than make changes to the process, this book serves as a reminder to ensure that magnesium is in the designer's arsenal. The raw material is twice as expensive as aluminium, but this is not insurmountable. With good design and engineering, a magnesium part can be produced to match the equivalent aluminium part in cost. The secret is to make sure the part is developed as a magnesium part and not as an aluminium part, which is a common mistake that is made in most industries. A well-designed magnesium part can match any aluminium part's cost easily, as the magnesium part uses less volume and weight. If the part is half the weight, then the material is cost neutralised.

Meridian and BCU's hope is that demand for magnesium increases, reducing the price, as was the case for aluminium. If the smelting industry invests in its production then magnesium prices will decrease in the same manner. It should be no more expensive to extract than aluminium, providing the same investment is made as usage increases. Aluminium is often accused as being over used and magnesium will play a big part in weight saving developments in the future.

---

[1] This foreword is adapted from an article by Simon Frost for Materials World, the members' magazine for the Institute of Materials, Minerals and Mining, in which Makhan Singh, Steve Brown and Randy Chalmers were interviewed. View article at bit.ly/2lWdBZY.

There are also many areas where the partnership is exploring quite radical and innovative thinking. For example, the STEAM (Science, Technology, Engineering, Arts and Mathematics) agenda at BCU is seeking to merge engineering with the arts – one of the outputs so far discussed has been creating a magnesium art installation to educate the wider public. The partnership is also interested in recovering heat from the magnesium die casting process production – example of the Abbey Stadium Leisure Centre in Worcestershire, which heats its swimming pool using waste heat from an adjacent crematorium. Other examples include the industrial ecology work that seeks to benchmark from the success of the British Sugar project, where CO_2 is used to grow tomatoes.

The partnership between BCU and Meridian Lightweight Technologies is innovative and exciting – indeed, several years from now, could we all be enjoying health benefits from magnesium enriched vegetables – grown at rapid pace, to feed an ever-growing global population?

Randy Chalmers
Makhan Singh
Simon Frost
July 2017

Randy Chalmers has over 20 years automotive experience working globally throughout Europe, Asia and North America at Meridian Lightweight Technologies in various roles. Randy has supported improvement activities in Process Engineering, Operations Management and Plant Management.

Makhan Singh has over 25 years automotive experience and was recently the Programme Manager at Meridian Lightweight Technologies working on the product launch for the Jaguar XE magnesium Front End Carrier and now works as the Development Manager for the Institute for Sustainable Futures at Birmingham City University.

Simon Frost is a journalist specialising in science communication. At the time of print for this first edition book, he is the departing Editor of Materials World, and the incoming Digital Editor for the Society of Chemical Industry. He has previously worked on a range of diverse titles.

Acknowledgements

The Editors would like to express their heartfelt thanks to the many authors who contributed to this volume and colleagues within Birmingham City University (BCU) for their support and engagement. It would be impossible to list all those who have contributed, but the Editors would like to acknowledge the support from the University's senior management most notably Professor Julian Beer, Joanna Birch, Dr Umar Daraz, Professor Melvyn Lees, Professor Keith Osman, Dr Nayan Patel, Professor Hanifa Shah, Anita Virk and Steven Wilkins.

Special thanks go to the organisations that have provided support and most notably:

- International Magnesium Association
- Forum of the Future
- The High Speed Sustainable Manufacturing Institute
- The Institution of Engineering and Technology

Finally, but not least, the Editors would like to recognise the support of Meridian Lightweight Technologies Inc who made this book possible with their foresight and engagement with BCU, especially Stephen Brown and Randy Chalmers.

Credits

Cover design by Claire Stevenson
Creative production by Catherine Davis and Rabia Bagurai
Project management by Makhan Singh
Conference Photographs by Nick Robinson

Contents

Foreword   iv
Randy Chalmers, Makhan Singh and Simon Frost

Acknowledgements

Magnesium: A Structural Super-Metal   3
Stephen Brown

A Perspective: Potential Growth in the Global Magnesium Industry -
Environmental Impacts and Recyclability   6
Martyn Alderman

STEAM Intelligence and its Relationship to Magnesium   15
Edmund Chadwick, Makhan Singh, Ethan Connor and Anita Virk

Supporting Women in Science and Engineering with BCU   22
and Meridian Lightweight Technologies Ltd
Laura Leyland

Attitudes Towards the Use of Magnesium Alloys by Engineers   27
Panagiotis Rentzelas and Eirini Mavritsaki

What it Means to Innovate: Vulnerabilities and Risks   30
Clayton Shaw

Magnesium and Mobility:
Investigating the Metal's Potential Role in a Low-Carbon Transport Industry   34
Michaela Rose

Design Optimisation for Magnesium Parts Used in Automotive Body Structure   39
Abed Alaswad

Towards Improvement of Formability of Magnesium Alloys   44
Michal Krzyzanowski, Janusz Majta, Krzysztof Muszka, Marta Slezak and David Randman

Magnesium Alloy Die Casting Process Improvement Using the
Single Minute Exchange of Dies (SMED) Method and Other Techniques   53
Alan Pendry

Downtime Solutions to High Pressure Die Casts (HPDC) Exchange
in Meridian Lightweight Technologies   58
Fawaz Annaz, Ian Hawkins and Steve Howard

Evaluation of a Strut Top Mount for a Magnesium Space
Frame Structure for Mainstream Road Cars   65
Richard Cornish

A Testbed Platform for UAV Emergency Deployment 71
Fawaz Annaz, Ian Hawkins and Steve Howard

Safety and Energy Assessment on Magnesium-Based Car Parts 76
Junfeng Yang, Muhammad Arslan and Kieran Jones

An Assessment of Lightweight Vehicles to Reduce Greenhouse Gas Emissions
with Focus on Magnesium 84
Siddharth Suhas Kulkarni and Jose Ricardo Sodre

Final Thoughts: Reflection & Conclusion 92
Makhan Singh and Martyn Alderman

Author Index

Subject Index (by Keywords)

Notes

Technical Papers

Magnesium: A Structural Super-Metal

Stephen Brown

Meridian Lightweight Technologies, Sutton-In-Ashfield, Nottingham, Orchard Way,
Calladine Park, Sutton-in-Ashfield, Nottinghamshire, NG17 1JU, UK.
Email: sbrown@meridian-mag.com

Abstract

Meridian Lightweight Technologies UK (MLTUK) are part of Meridian Technologies Inc., which is part of the Wanfeng Auto Holding Group. MLTUK are the leading full-service supplier of innovative lightweight magnesium die cast components and assemblies in the global automotive market. MLTUK was set up in 1999 and have a passion for magnesium - regularly campaigning for industry and engineers to have a better understanding of magnesium to allow it to take its rightful place alongside other less suitable structural materials in use today. MLTUK is working in partnership with Birmingham City University (BCU) to improve industry understanding and assist in increasing the opportunities across the industry spectrum. Academics at BCU will provide Meridian and industry with a greater scope of application ideas.

Keywords
Magnesium, Strength, Aluminium

WHY MAGNESIUM?

Magnesium is a fascinating metal, which if designed and optimised in the correct manner, will provide an enhanced strength, stiffness and stability, and will deliver a higher specific yield strength and specific modulus than nearly all other structural metals. Magnesium is the eighth most abundant natural metal and is the 11th most abundant material by mass in the human body, an essential ingredient. Its excellent strength/stiffness to weight ratio surpasses most other natural metals, allowing it to be a metal of choice when developing for structurally very light products. Magnesium is up to 50% lighter than aluminium, stiff, energy efficient and recyclable natural material for our modern-day design needs. It is the lightest structural metal available. It occurs naturally in sea water and sea water actually contains 12 billion pounds per cubic mile. Magnesium is an alkaline earth metal, but unlike the other alkaline earth metals, an oxygen-free environment is unnecessary for storage because magnesium is protected by a thin layer of oxide that is fairly impermeable and difficult to remove. Magnesium has the lowest melting (923 K (1,202 °F)) and the lowest boiling point (1,363 K (1,994 °F)) of all the alkaline earth metals[2]. Magnesium reacts with water at room temperature, and hydrogen bubbles form slowly on the surface. If powdered, this reaction happens much more readily, and with higher temperatures. Magnesium's reversible reaction with water can be harnessed to store energy and run a magnesium-based engine.

ADVANTAGES IN CAST APPLICATIONS

Magnesium alloys are being used today in many automotive structural applications both external and internal, such as cross car beams and front-end carriers that support the front of the vehicle as well as the headlamp. Many of these castings are the full width of the vehicle and are single cast components. If the integration is considered during the design phases then

---

[2] Magnesium properties obtained from NORSK HYDRO - 2001

savings can be made in incorporating further components into the design reducing the componentry and assembly costs.

Magnesium has an excellent tool life when compared to the most common of cast materials, aluminium, with up to 2x longer and flows far better, which enables engineers to design even thinner wall castings with much more detail, such as company logos, *etc*. The design will likely last the life of the die due to its excellent flow properties. It is by mass, one third lighter than aluminium and a good magnesium design would be half the weight of its equivalent aluminium design.

Magnesium is easily machined and has an excellent tool life. It is very flexible for design purposes, and offers the best dimensional capability of most structural materials. It has an unbeatable strength to weight ratio when measured against any natural metal in the periodic table, so is perfect for structural applications. Magnesium also offers a magnificent stiffness capability with ranges of elongation across the alloy ranges allowing bespoke designs to meet most structural needs.

Its energy management properties allow it to be easily developed for increased performance targets (NVH, Frequency). Its heat dissipation properties are so good it is often classified as a flame retardant material, as it dissipates its heat across its mass so readily, it allows more time before the flammable material surrounding it can ignite. Magnesium also has a high electrical conductivity, but is not magnetic.

Magnesium is a natural material, so readily available and recyclable and is not, as often depicted, a corrosive material. It has similar oxidisation properties to aluminium and castings simply turn an irregular darker colour as they oxidise.

CONSIDERATIONS DURING DESIGN

It is important to remember that this is magnesium and **not** aluminium. The materials are nothing at all like each other, so when designing one must always design *for* magnesium with no other material in mind. It is also a casting so ensure at the very least you have personnel that have experience in cast technologies. It never ceases to amaze the author how OEMs today are taking on increased design responsibility and ending up with monstrous parts that have been ill-designed, with appalling attachment strategies that do not take into account some basic design considerations that must be adopted when designing for cast parts.

Part of developing attachment strategies for magnesium, or any other casting for that matter, one should try to use the thread "forming" type attachment so we maximise the value in a one-piece cast design. This would mean utilising the attachments actually designed for magnesium. However, galvanic corrosion needs to be understood, or you will experience galvanic corrosion if you expose a magnesium product to the elements constantly with Fe based attachments. This must be both constant elemental attack and Fe based attachments. Either one of these in isolation will NOT see galvanic corrosion, simply aesthetic oxidisation. To design in magnesium one needs to understand these distinctions and design accordingly. Avoidance is both simple and easy, often requiring a simple aluminium washer to prevent any, even minor, reaction.

CONCLUSION

Magnesium is without doubt a most remarkable material, and its usage will accelerate rapidly as industry discovers more applications across a variety of disciplines. One must always remember that to optimise the application of magnesium components – one must only design *for* magnesium with no other material in mind.

A Perspective: Potential Growth in the Global Magnesium Industry – Environmental Impacts and Recyclability

Martyn Alderman

International Magnesium Association, European Committee Chairman
Email: martyn.alderman@magnesium-elektron.com

Abstract

Magnesium enjoyed considerable growth in the last decade of the twentieth century due to an increase in automotive die casting alloy applications for light-weighting. In spite of considerable research activity into wrought applications in the last fifteen years, the use of sheet and extrusions is largely limited to non-structural applications, primary batteries and small electronic devices (cameras, cell phones, lap-tops and tablets), and cathodic protection. The major volume use for magnesium metal remains as an alloying element for aluminium, and as a chemical reducing or microstructure modifying agent in the production of titanium, steel and Spheroidal Graphite (SG) iron. Powders are currently used in organic chemical reactions and as pyrotechnic devices rather than for any structural purpose, however, applications in energy storage devices continue to be actively pursued, and bioresorbable implants are beginning to gain market acceptance. The International Magnesium Association (IMA) exists to promote the end uses of magnesium and to represent the industry as a whole in issues that affect its members. In the last 5 years, the IMA has sponsored a Life Cycle Study for magnesium being used in automotive and aerospace applications, a video to promote wider application of the metal and an End of Life Scrap Study for the European Market. In spite of projected compound annual growth rates (CAGRs) of 6-8% for the next 10 years, today's global consumption of the metal remains less than 1 million tonnes and less than 2% of the size of the global aluminium market. This industry size today presents a challenge for the European economy to promote the end of life recovery of the metal using fully functional recycling rather than allowing magnesium to be removed in aluminium refining operations.

Keywords
Markets, Life Cycle, End of Life

THE MAGNESIUM MARKET

The major volume use for magnesium metal in the European Union (EU) remains as an alloying element for aluminium (in can-stock, and structural alloys) and as a microstructure modifying agent in the production of steel and nodular cast iron (see Figure 1). The most significant structural field of application of magnesium alloys is in the field of automotive die castings, where the mass saving and consequent fuel efficiency provide a life cycle benefit in terms of reduced carbon dioxide emissions, although this life cycle benefit is very dependent upon the source of primary energy. For global economic reasons, there is no primary production today in Europe and so the source of the imported primary magnesium is significant here. This is discussed later in this paper.

In the aerospace industry, although the light-weighting benefit of magnesium in large castings is exploited in the rotorcraft industry to enhance performance, payload and time on station, the use of magnesium in commercial fixed wing structures declined in the 1970's with increasing engine power and concern about corrosion and flammability. Ten years of work were required to change the opinion of the Federal Aviation Authority in the United States about the acceptability of magnesium inside the aircraft cabin ultimately resulting in the "magnesium alloys must not be used" statement being removed from SAE AS8049C (Lyon, Gwynne 2015). This is also discussed further in the section on Life Cycle Benefits.

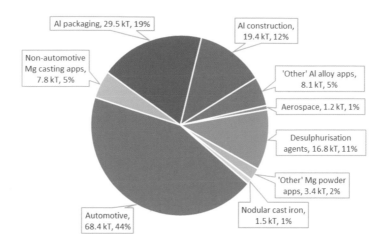

FIGURE 1: Magnesium applications in the EU in 2012 (Oakdene Hollins 2017 Study).

There are, however, other applications for magnesium alloys beyond aerospace and automotive; we continue to see a significant number of published papers in the field of magnesium biotechnology, and the IMA gave its Process Award in 2017 in Singapore to a bioresorabable alloy system for use in bone pins and screws (IMA Awards 2017). The medical sector is however a very tightly regulated environment and the barriers to entry remain high and volumes extremely low. There are certainly good applications in cardiac stents, bone plates and wires for those at the forefront of the technology, but volumes in this market sector will never demand a new smelter.

The technical and economic press talk incessantly about the game changing nature of 3D printing or Additive Layer Manufacturing in our world, and with the emerging availability of magnesium alloy powders, the potential for lightweight innovative structures incorporating magnesium alloys is being explored. The IMA gave its Process Award in 2016 in Rome to a Laser Powder Bed Additive process that had jointly been jointly developed between Laser Zentrum Hannover and Magnesium Elektron. The key markets here are likely to be specialist aerospace (with the emphasis on space) applications and on the biomedical sector for customized implants.

The Magnesium Industry continues to need innovation in alloy design to remain competitive with alternative materials, and understanding deformation mechanisms in alloy systems with limited room temperature ductility and methods of reducing anisotropy and asymmetry remain important in widening structural applications whether it be for automotive or aerospace (Luo, 2017). The major focus of technical publications over the past 15 years has been in this field rather than in the more widely utilized area of automotive die casting, although work continues on lower cost, more corrosion and creep resistant alloys (Abbott, 2017).

Ultimately magnesium alloys must be affordable in their target market, so it makes sense to continue development work in the field of twin roll casting and room temperature formable alloys for the automotive industry, but as the aerospace industry has demonstrated in the past, a lowering in fuel prices impacts behaviour. In today's economy, it appears that only when CAFÉ or EU CO_2 emission standards demand it will the issues of incorporating mixed materials into vehicles be addressed to allow magnesium sheet use beyond internal closure type components. There has been talk of electric vehicles needing increased range driving light-weighting, and at the IMA's most recent conference in Singapore there was a message that the need for battery electric vehicles in China, to address growing demand for personal mobility whilst not exceeding available hydrocarbon resources, might lead to a wider use of magnesium in structure to offset the weight of the battery, however, at the same time existing transmission applications might be eliminated reducing magnesium die casting demand (Tauber, Jaschinsky 2017). Today the average consumption of magnesium per vehicle in China is 1.5- 3.4kg. There is a target to increase this to 45kg by 2030 which would demand 1.7 million tonnes of magnesium.

The magnesium industry caught a cold in 2008 after the Beijing Olympics when uncertainty over supply drove prices beyond the expectations of the automotive industry, which was then hit by a global economic crisis. Nine years later, the European and North American automotive industries are again considering magnesium for programmes that are 5 years out, the technology challenges remain achieving Class A surfaces for sheet, and integration technologies off the back of a small installed base of suppliers. There also remains the question whether extrusion productivity and asymmetry of properties can be addressed adequately to make magnesium extrusions competitive with aluminium for transport applications in both the automotive and rail sectors.

At the IMA Conference in Singapore, work carried out in Japan and South Korea (Hirano, Bong 2017) on the development of extruded alloys for large rail section components was presented which are being encouraged by the Japanese Government, but the installed infrastructure to produce these large sections is very limited outside of Russia and China. Magnesium market consumption at 843,000 tonnes in 2016 still remains at only 1.7% of global aluminium consumption making it difficult for wrought capacity expansions to be justified unless underwritten by a major supply contract.

The market analysts at CM Group however remain optimistic that the industry will see 6.4% CAGR between 2016 and 2026. Global market consumption was stated as aluminium alloying at 37%, die casting at 32% (28% Auto, 4% other), 15% going into the Fe/steel industry, 10% to the Ti industry, leaving 6% for all other markets. On future growth, C&M saw 10% CAGR in automotive sheet, 4.7% in aluminium alloying, whilst ferrous industry demand would remain flat (Grandfield, 2017).

LIFE CYCLE ANALYSIS

The International Magnesium Association exists for the benefit of its members to try to grow the applications of magnesium across the World. In the face of increasing environmental scrutiny from end users, in particular due to the fact the 83% of the World's primary magnesium was being produced in China, the IMA commissioned the German Aerospace and Automotive Research Centre in Stuttgart (DLR) to carry out a cradle-to-grave analysis of the use of magnesium in a typical automotive die casting application (steering wheel armature) and in a sand cast commercial aerospace assembly (door closures). The study by Ehrenberger (2013) considered the two main primary production processes which were the Pidgeon Process (reduction of calcined dolomite with ferrosilicon) in China, and the Electrolytic Process (from dehydrated magnesium chloride) being performed in Israel and in the USA.

The life cycle inventory for the production via Pidgeon process in China was based on 2011. With recent changes in processing coal was only used for the calcination process. For other process steps, coke oven, semi-coke oven, producer or natural gas are used, and a large proportion of these gases arise as by-products from other processes. The production of ferrosilicon (FeSi), the calcination of dolomite and the reduction itself are the most GHG-emission intensive life cycle steps. The weighted result for greenhouse gas emission of the Pidgeon process in 2011 was 25.8 kg CO_2eq / kg Mg. This was a significant reduction from a previous study (2008) where the value was 43 kg CO_2eq / kg Mg. The ISO 14044 standard gives a preference to system expansion or dividing unit processes instead of allocation in case of multifunctional processes. As coke oven and semi-coke oven gas are waste from (semi) coke production, the use of such production waste can be credited to the primary magnesium production. By applying this approach, the weighted average GHG emissions of the Pidgeon process decreases to 19.9 kg CO_2eq / kg Mg.

In the IMA study, we developed a model for an electrolysis which represents today's conditions. The electrolysis model was specific for the production of magnesium in Israel. Electrolysis plants in Russia (where the magnesium produced is used in titanium reduction) are based on carnallite as well and in the carnallite based electrolysis plant, two by-products are produced: liquefied chlorine (Cl_2) and KCl-rich salt. The first has a wide range of potential uses and the second one can be converted to potassium fertilizer. The production of these by-products is credited as they substitute for the production of the material from other routes. For the global warming potential, the overall emissions amount to 17.8 kg CO_2eq / kg Mg. If the substitution of the production of the by-products in other processes is credited in the impact assessment, the GWP results decrease slightly to 14 kg CO_2eq / kg Mg.

A study carried out in relation to the Qinghai electrolytic smelter project in China (Jun, 2017), which is due to come on stream in 2017, has predicted its emissions to be as low as 6.5 kg CO_2eq / kg Mg because of a mix of solar and wind energy (renewable) which make up 85% of the electricity usage. This plant will have 100,000 tonnes of capacity as built and has scope for expansion to 450,000 tonnes. If the market growth does not occur as predicted and this capacity replaces existing Pidgeon process smelting in China it will have a significant effect on the "global warming impact" of Chinese magnesium exports.

For the ecological assessment of the use of lightweight materials in transport, the use phase has considerable influence on the overall balance. The magnesium steering wheel part was compared to a steering wheel made from aluminium. Fuel savings were calculated for a midsize passenger car operated with petrol for a mileage of 200,000 km. A fuel reduction coefficient of 0.35l / 100kg * 100km was used for the lighter weight magnesium part. The sum of emissions from production and end-of-life of the magnesium steering wheel were subtracted from the emission of the aluminium component. The results were based on a combination of GHG emissions from the average Pidgeon process and electrolysis (83% Pidgeon process and 17% electrolysis assumed). For the aluminium reference, a world average emission value was used for electrolysis as source of primary metal.

The results (Figure 2) showed a positive net balance of CO_2eq emissions for all magnesium production scenarios. The lowest advantage is reached when magnesium from the Pidgeon process based on semi-coke oven gas is used as primary metal. Magnesium from electrolysis gives the highest savings of CO_2eq emissions. Further benefits in Life Cycle Analysis can be obtained if the end component is Functionally Recycled – this will be discussed in the next Section.

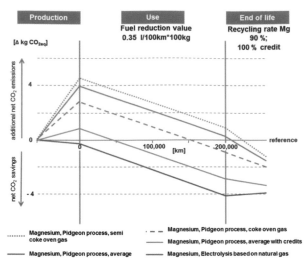

FIGURE 2: Overall balance for magnesium steering wheel compared to aluminium steering wheel based on a mileage of 200,000 km.

The use of the sand cast magnesium aircraft door parts was analysed for hypothetical application in an A320 aircraft. An example case study considered a flight over a distance of 4,100km to calculate the emissions during aircraft operation. The relation of aircraft weight and fuel consumption was calculated using the DLR model VAMPzero. The end-of-life of aircraft components was not part of the study as it is not considered to be relevant for the greenhouse gas emissions of this use case given the 30-year service life of a commercial airframe. In case of the comparison between aircraft parts of magnesium and aluminium, only a few flights were found to be necessary to reach a break-even point for the amortization of higher emissions during component production (Figure 3).

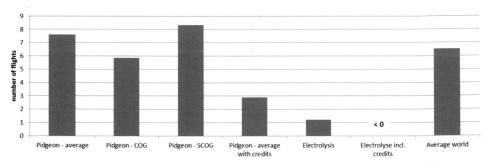

FIGURE 3: Number of flights for emission amortization for difference magnesium scenarios.

When magnesium is produced by electrolysis and the by-products are credited, the production of components has fewer emissions compared to the aluminium reference. For other magnesium scenarios, the break-even point was reached at latest during the ninth flight. Due to the high potential for fuel savings during the aircraft operation, the influence of component production and source of primary metal is insignificant. It was concluded that for a 22% weight difference (aluminium parts weighed 8.5kg vs. 6.63kg for the magnesium parts) the emission savings during the aircraft operation amounted to approximately 8t CO_2eq

per year. Assuming a life time of 30 years for an aircraft, the reduction potential for the magnesium components substituted was about 226 t CO_2eq.

END OF LIFE SCRAP STUDY

It is well understood in the aluminium industry that the primary extraction process (electrolysis) is the most energy intensive process, and if end of life scrap can be reused functionally this primary input energy may be reduced by 95%. This same argument is true for magnesium alloys that can also be functionally recycled at the end of life.

In 2013, the European Commission became concerned about the availability of certain "Critical Raw Materials (CRM)" that are not today produced from primary extraction in the EU. Magnesium is one of these materials and the EU commissioned Deloitte to carry out a Material Systems Analysis (MSA) to identify how much end of life material was being recycled for a number of CRMs including magnesium. In 2015, the published result of this study claimed that of the 167,000 tonnes of magnesium imported into the EU in 2012, some 114,000 tonnes ended up in landfill. This figure was contested by the IMA as being inaccurate, but without a detailed counter study, the IMA was unable to convince DG Grow of any error. As a consequence, in 2017, the IMA European Committee, supported by the Board of the IMA, commissioned Oakdene Hollins (a UK based consultancy firm) to review the MSA study and where appropriate point out any errors or false assumptions. A High-Level Sankey Diagram in Figure 4 below shows the results of the 2017 Study (Bell, 2017).

In addition to consultation with stakeholders, one major difference in this study was that it attempted to fully take account of the use of magnesium within the aluminium alloy lifecycle given that 40% of magnesium imported is used in aluminium alloying.

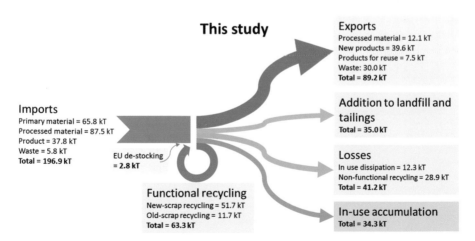

FIGURE 4: High level Sankey diagram for magnesium (metal) in the EU for the year 2012.

The main differences in the findings of this study compared to those reported in the MSA study:

- The figure for magnesium imports into the EU is 18% higher than reported in the MSA study.

- Exports, which include vehicles exported at end of life, are over double those identified in the MSA study.
- Landfill in the EU at 35,000t is only 30% of that identified in the MSA study.
- The MSA study includes only old scrap functional recycling, while this study also quantified functional recycling of new scrap at 51,700t. This is significant as die casting is the principal structural use of magnesium, and 50% of die cast output is Class 1 scrap (runner systems and biscuits/pucks) that can be readily recycled with 5% energy consumption relative to primary magnesium, and relatively small melt losses.
- Non-functional recycling of magnesium at 29,000t is an order of magnitude higher than in the MSA study. This accounts for the use of desulphurisation slags and aluminium drosses in construction and mineral wool production.
- Instead of 9,000t of de-accumulation as in the MSA study, this study found there were 34,000t of in-use magnesium accumulation. Annually about 14,000 tonnes of magnesium is being accumulated in automotive vehicles in use (Figure 5: in 2012 about 4.14kg per vehicle, as compared with 3.13kg in 2002). In addition, there is an annual accumulation of about 15,000t of magnesium in aluminium alloys used in construction that have a life in excess of 40 years.

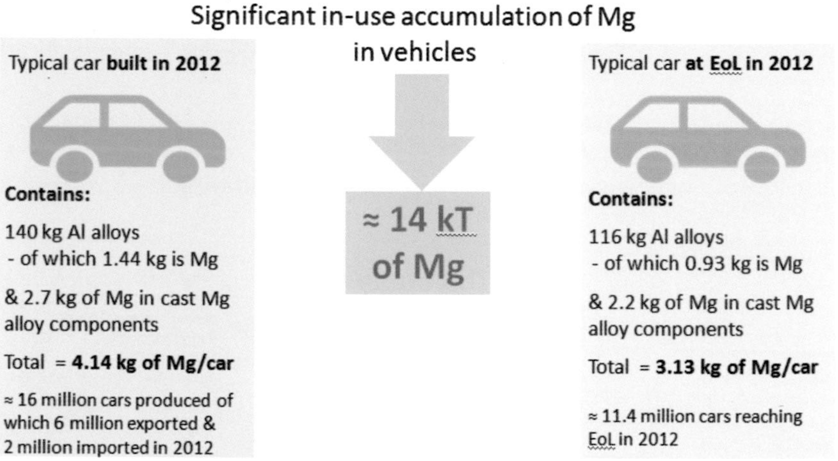

Significant in-use accumulation of Mg in vehicles

Typical car built in 2012

Contains:

140 kg Al alloys
- of which 1.44 kg is Mg

& 2.7 kg of Mg in cast Mg alloy components

Total = **4.14 kg of Mg/car**

≈ 16 million cars produced of which 6 million exported & 2 million imported in 2012

≈ **14 kT** **of Mg**

Typical car at EoL in 2012

Contains:

116 kg Al alloys
- of which 0.93 kg is Mg

& 2.2 kg of Mg in cast Mg alloy components

Total = **3.13 kg of Mg/car**

≈ 11.4 million cars reaching EoL in 2012

FIGURE 5: Accumulation of magnesium in vehicles in use equivalent to 14,000 tpa.

The End of Life - Recycling Input Rate (EoL-RIR) for magnesium in the EU was also derived from the material flow analysis data. This is an important ratio as it indicates how much of today's magnesium industry dependency could be "self-sufficient" if raw material supplies were cut off by political action outside of the EU.

At 7% the EoL-RIR of magnesium is low, lower than that of aluminium at 12% (global, not EU specific value). This was not unexpected given the dispersive nature of some of magnesium's applications, and the collection and recycling inefficiencies discussed in more detail below. The main improvements in collection and recycling efficiencies that could increase the recycling rate of magnesium are:

- Greater dismantling of aluminium and magnesium alloy components from ELVs.
- Even higher collection rate of EoL aluminium beverage cans.

- Technological advances in the automated sorting of aluminium alloy fractions from shredding.
- Diverting more high magnesium-containing aluminium alloys to remelters, who generally try to retain the magnesium in their input materials, rather than by refiners, who do not.
- Diverting more segregated EoL magnesium alloys to specialist magnesium recyclers, and potentially developing of magnesium casting alloys that are more tolerant of Ni, Cu and other contaminants from fasteners (e.g., AZC531 or AZC1231).
- Better slag utilisation by the aluminium and steel industries (non-functional recycling).

This list highlights the fact that the recycling rate of magnesium is very dependent on the activities of the aluminium and, to a lesser extent, the steel industries. Identifying best practice for magnesium retention in aluminium alloy recycling requires further investigation in order to identify more targeted opportunities for its improvement. It would also be interesting to calculate what the maximum realistic recycling rate of magnesium would be in the EU if current, and forecast, best practice methods for magnesium retention were fully implemented.

CONCLUSIONS

In spite of this reliance on other industries, the author predicts that magnesium recycling in the EU is increasing. Even since 2012, the baseline year for this study, the collection rate of EoL aluminium beverage cans has increased and there are policies being enacted, such as research into new technologies, to improve the competitiveness of ELV processors. The policies concerning ELVs are driven by the ambitious recycling targets for ELVs in the EU. Meeting these targets is reliant on a strong ELV processing sector. However, the sector is facing an overall decline in the steel content of vehicles, which is a problem as the plastics and composites they are partly being replaced with are typically of a lower value and more difficult to recycle. The material and value extraction from the aluminium and magnesium alloys in ELVs will help offset the decrease in revenue from steel and contribute to the EU achieving its ELV recycling targets.

Acknowledgements
The author would like to thank the Simone Ehrenberger at DLR and Nia Bell at Oakdene Hollins for their respective content in this summary paper, and the IMA European Committee for the opportunity to present this content. The views expressed in this paper are those of the author and do not necessarily represent those of the International Magnesium Association. Both studies referenced in this paper were sponsored by the International Magnesium Association and its members for the benefit of the magnesium industry.

References
Abbott, T. (2017). Magontec, development of new magnesium die casting alloys. IMA Proceedings, Singapore. http://www.intlmag.org/?page=2017_Conf_handouts
Bell, N. (2017). Magnesium recycling in the EU. Oakdene Hollins (to be published) http://www.intlmag.org/
Bong, S. Y. (2017). KIMS, new application of corrosion resistant non-flammable magnesium alloys. IMA Proceedings, Singapore. http://www.intlmag.org/?page=2017_Conf_handouts
Ehrenberger, S. (2013). DLR.
http://c.ymcdn.com/sites/intlmag.site-ym.com/resource/resmgr/docs/lca/2013IMA_LCAStudy_Summary.pdf
Grandfield, J. (2017). Global primary magnesium supply and demand balance. CM Group. IMA Proceedings, Singapore. http://www.intlmag.org/?page=2017_Conf_handouts
Hirano, S. (2017). Today's magnesium technologies and applications in Japan. JMA. IMA Proceedings, Singapore. http://www.intlmag.org/?page=2017_Conf_handouts

IMA Awards (2017). http://www.intlmag.org/?page=2017_awards_ima

Jaschinsky, W. (2017). Is magnesium ready for the next revolution? Remag Leichtmetall Gmbh. IMA Proceedings, Singapore. http://www.intlmag.org/?page=2017_Conf_handouts

Jun, W. S. (2017). Magnesium fosters green magnesium industry. QSLIC. IMA Proceedings, Singapore. http://www.intlmag.org/?page=2017_Conf_handouts

Luo, A. (2017). Enhancing the ductility of cast and wrought magnesium alloy products. Ohio State University. IMA Proceedings, Singapore. http://www.intlmag.org/?page=2017_Conf_handouts

Lyon, P. and Gwynne, B. (2015). https://www.fire.tc.faa.gov/pdf/materials/Feb15Meeting/Lyon-0215-ModifiedAircraftSeats.pdf

Tauber, M. (2017). The Chinese automotive market - much more than only the largest market in the World. Fauris. IMA Proceedings, Singapore. http://www.intlmag.org/?page=2017_Conf_handouts

STEAM Intelligence and its Relationship to Magnesium

Edmund Chadwick, Makhan Singh[*3] , Ethan Connor[*] and Anita Virk[*]

School of Computing, Science & Engineering, University of Salford, Newton Building, Salford, Greater Manchester, M5 4WT, UK.
[*]Birmingham City University, 15 Bartholomew Row, Birmingham B5 5JU, UK.
Email: makhan.singh@bcu.ac.uk

Abstract
An Emotional Nerve Intelligence module for second year mathematics undergraduates is presented as a case study. This is a new concept that extends Emotional Intelligence by including psychotherapy practices used to control nerves (anxiety and stress). The use of such an intervention (*i.e.* psychotherapy that resides within the arts subject area) and applying it within a STEM setting, has led to an outcome of STEAM intelligence. This is delivered within a mathematics STEM setting with the aim of releasing the undergraduates' potential. Results show development in self-awareness of the students by capturing pre- and post-comments, and anecdotal observations indicating the success in students developing their ability to think for themselves are also given. The importance of magnesium to the human diet and its relationship to STEAM intelligence is also explored.

Keywords
Emotional Intelligence, Soft Skills, Curriculum Innovation

INTRODUCTION

Employability skills include the soft skills based around communication, and this is of utmost importance for employers to access the highly technical and specialised disciplines in the STEM (Science, Technology, Engineering and Mathematics) sector. This has been noted upon by Toland (2011) who reflects on the importance of a T-shaped skills set, where the depth of the technical knowledge is enhanced by the horizontal ability to apply knowledge, and this ability is increasingly being seen as of critical importance for the STEM disciplines. This sentiment is also supported by the UK Commission for Employment & Skills UKCES (2010), which highlights an existing and anticipated future demand for the provision of higher level skills for managers and professionals. Considerable strides have been made by Higher Education Institutions (HEIs) to incorporate development of these soft skills into their courses, with support from Government initiatives such as the National HE STEM Programme and also from the professional bodies, in the case of mathematics the Institute of Mathematics and its Applications (IMA). For example, through this support Chadwick *et al.* (2011; 2012a) developed a novel Business and Industrial Mathematics module for the undergraduate mathematics degree programme at the University of Salford, which aims to develop and assess working practices for mathematicians and tackle such issues as soft skills communication, careers and EI (Emotional Intelligence). A booklet of good practice edited by Chadwick and Singh (2012) details HEI good practice and how to implement it in the area of employability skills in the mathematical sciences, and similarly a more academic study is given by Waldock and Rowlett (2012).

---

[3] Author to whom any correspondence should be addressed.

Savoley and Mayer (1990) describe EI as *"the subset of social intelligence that involves the ability to monitor one's own and others' feelings and emotions, to discriminate among them and to use this information to guide one's thinking and actions"*. In recent years, studies have examined the role of Emotional Intelligence in education. The results of these suggest that low Emotional Intelligence has a relationship to a higher level of unauthorised absences and lateness in secondary school children (Petrides *et al.*, 2004). In both school and HEI students, a relationship has been established between academic achievement and ability and Emotional Intelligence by Qualter, Gardner and Whiteley (2007). They further state that EI is essential in the development of students at their HEI through their Personal Development Plan (PDP). Emotional intelligence is in essence the ability to understand and manage emotions - it can be learnt and developed. Self-motivation, communicating effectively, empathizing with others, overcoming challenges and defusing conflict are key attributes of good emotional intelligence.

Is there STEAM Intelligence?

Appreciation of the STEAM (Science, Technology, Engineering, Arts and Mathematics) agenda and its potential for generating radical and innovative thinking is making significant strides in the worlds of industry, commerce, the arts and education. To excel in this brave new world of STEAM requires an openness to new knowledge bases from a multitude of diverse disciplines and, as one of Carl Sagan's quote illustrates (*"if you want to make an apple pie from scratch, you must first create the universe"*), an ability to think outside of the box (or even do away with notions of traditional and potentially reductive discipline defined boxes in the first place). However, this trend raises a question for educationalists and employers: is there a form of thinking that could be described as STEAM intelligence? And if so, is it genuinely something new or simply a re-calibrating and restructuring of pre-existing concepts and approaches? And if it is a discernible phenomenon, can it be taught and encouraged? And what exactly, you may be asking, does all of this have to do with magnesium anyway? Well, aside from the considerable innovations at play within the chapters of this book in relation to magnesium's many uses and applications, there is potentially another level of relevance at play here; one both literal and figurative; biologic and symbolic.

From Connectivism to Trans-disciplinarianism to EI

The ability to identify connections between seemingly disparate fields and disciplines is a core concept to this book. As Clayton Shaw suggests in his chapter on 'What it Means to Innovate' we are now living in a world where the strides made in technology and communications create ever greater opportunities (and need) for not just inter-disciplinary, but trans-disciplinary approaches to discovery, innovation and their commercial and cultural application. The STEAMhouse project at BCU represents the creation of a formal space in which to actively nurture such inter and trans-disciplinary strands and create a unique creative arena for innovations to not just occur, but thrive.

There are certainly precedents in the literature for what could be conceived of as a STEAM intelligence. Kelly's (2016) conceptualisation of a 'digital socialism' and net-worked world echoes the influential works of educationalists Siemens (2006) and Downes (2005) who argue old theories of social constructivism are no longer inclusive and wide ranging enough to accurately reflect how knowledge is generated in the contemporary world. Instead they posit Connectivism as a new theory for knowledge generation. Learning and knowledge they argue rests more literally than ever in a diversity of opinions. Knowledge is about a person's connective capacity and learning becomes the process of navigating and connecting specialized networks and information sources. Learning is not simply achieved through a network, the learning they suggest is in many ways the inter-connectivity of network itself (Stewart, 2015). Such thinking aligns too with Jenkins (2006) concept of a 'participatory culture' in which we are both potentially consumers and creators of content.

There are links here to be drawn too with the substantial body of literature published on creativity and innovation and by implication, emotional intelligence. Oman *et al.* (2013) investigating ways to evaluate stages of creativity in engineering design processes present an overview of the theories pertaining to creativity. Citing Sternberg (1988) they note that traditionally creativity can be divided into the four categories of environment, product, process, and person and that this latter category of person can further sub-divided into psychometric and cognitive aspects.

This cognitive aspect is significant to a proposed concept of STEAM intelligence because as Cropley and Cropley (2005) argue creativity is defined not by *convergent thinking* (a form of thinking which is the direct opposite of creative thinking, focusing as it does solely on existing facts and not deviating from pre-defined instructions), but instead by *divergent thinking*. That is, thinking that involves a "branching out" from given assumptions to generate and explore new possibilities; possibilities which may even appear counter intuitive or illogical if viewed solely through a single discipline specific lens but which, when pursued, result in innovations and potentially paradigm shifting perspectives. There are very clear links in the process just described to the ways of working involved in a STEAM related project. Most strikingly the ability to not just embrace, but perhaps actively seek out champions of divergent thinking and new perspectives from trans-disciplinary sources. However, alongside such endeavours comes the need for an openness to undertake risks, to tolerate ambiguity and be reflexively self-aware of, and manage feelings of insecurity or uncertainty that traversing unknown territories may generate. Additionally, there will be of course the need to work well with others and communicate and cooperate as part of a multi-disciplinary team. All of these attributes call not just on abilities in the cognitive domain, but in the affective domain also, and broadly fall into the array of intra and interpersonal skills often termed emotional intelligence (EI) (Goleman, 1995).

So Why the Link to Magnesium?
Aside from the many commercial applications explored in this book, magnesium plays a crucial role in over 300 functions in the human body including the metabolism of food, synthesis of fatty acids and proteins, and the transmission of nerve impulses (De Baaji, 2015). Additionally, a growing body of research indicates that appropriate levels of magnesium are critical for robust physical and mental health and contribute to a wide number of health variables, including (but not restricted to) anxiety reduction (Sartori *et al.*, 2012); reduced risk of heart disease (Hruby *et al.*, 2014); diabetes prevention and management (Dong *et al.*, 2011) bone density and overall skeletal health (Castigloni, 2013). Further studies indicate it plays a key role in suppression of inflammatory responses in the body and assists in various aspects of neurological functioning from the reduction of depression and migraines to improved mental acuity and memory (De Baajj *et al.*, 2015; Slutsky *et al.*, 2010).

Magnesium's role in the body is, it appears, even more influential than originally thought. It acts frequently in a way that could be viewed as a facilitator or enabler for the human bodies' many different systems and functions. In this regard it is a rather interesting choice for a STEAMhouse related project, as it is an apt symbol for what applications of STEAM intelligence seek to achieve: to bring together and facilitate better functioning of a wide variety of systems, professionals and artisans in collaboration, and rather appropriately if these individuals have the recommended levels of magnesium in their bodies whilst collaborating it may even help them think better and feel less stressed while they are doing so!

Case Study of STEAM Intelligence: An Emotional Intelligence Module for Mathematics
Although the incorporation of soft skills within the curriculum for HE STEM disciplines including mathematics is well under way in the UK, and student ability in this area is generally being attributed to good EI, there is little curriculum development on the use of EI in STEM courses. With this in mind, and using his skills and experiences as a psychotherapist and from his time in industry as an engineering manager, as well as working for the IMA, Singh developed an EI module specifically aimed at Mathematics (and STEM) undergraduates for raising employability skills. In this module, Singh emphasized those aspects of EI useful for mathematicians. These were identified from his work in the HEI mathematics community over the past 6 years, and from the CBI report (2010), where employers surveyed identified generic 'employability skills' as a non-discipline specific priority for business when recruiting graduates and indicated that STEM graduates in particular were not 'demonstrating' these at recruitment. These generic skills as defined by the CBI include self-management, team working, communication and literacy. At Salford, there is a dedicated module for the development of these generic skills. Having a dedicated module enables the trailing of new practices, which can then be developed and integrated into other modules. Examples include the development of teamwork and modelling which were first trialled in this module and are now integrated into many modules in the degree programme. Emotional Intelligence was trialled in a component of this module in 2013/14 by Singh and Chadwick (2015) with particular emphasis on the following module student outcomes:

- Develop a self-awareness of the inner self
- Learn to engage in self reflection

This component was run over one full day per week over a period of 3 weeks, and consisted of three sessions of group work each lasting four hours, as well as coursework, further study and examination making up 40 hours. The group sessions were held them in flat rooms, with the lecture room set up with chairs in a circle for a class size of 20, creating a room more traditionally associated with counselling studies.

The method of assessment for the EI component was structured around a 20-minute class test (20%); one coursework assignment (40%) and a reflective journal (40%). The class test assignment was themed around the students writing their own obituary – the purpose of which was to engage the students to develop their self-awareness and self-reflection, as well as developing their ability to articulate thoughts and ideas in a small period of time. The coursework assignment was titled 'Conversation with Self', where students were tasked with engaging with themselves through written 'self-conversation' - this is a technique from Gestalt therapy given in Perls (1973), an existential/experiential form of psychotherapy that emphasizes personal responsibility, and that focuses upon the individual's experience in the present moment. The final assessment was a reflective journal – designed to capture the learning process the student has been through over the past three weeks; again, developing the student's ability to engage in self-reflection. As Emotional Intelligence is a soft (rather than hard) skill, the marking was more akin to arts rather than sciences (*i.e.* no actual 'correct' answer).

Results and Observations

Each week the attendance numbers increased – week one saw 12 students attending; week two saw 14 students and the final week saw a full house of 20 students. The module evaluation feedback had very positive feedback from the staff and students, although this evidence is qualitative. However, a longitudinal study shall be attempted later to see the impact of this module to actual student grades versus predicted grades – and to see if the module has had any major impact, as well as looking in the future to student destination data. To give an indication of the feedback, one positive and one negative comment is given below:

'This was an excellent module – I would definitely choose to do this module if it were an option in my final year'

'Can't understand why we had to do this module – I signed up for a maths degree – not feelings and emotions'.

As the module was held over a short space of time, it was difficult to assess long term impact evaluation, however, Singh did devise an *Emotional Shift Measurement, i.e.* pre-entry question and a post exit question to assess what shift or change had occurred in the students in terms of developing emotional intelligence. The students were asked at the beginning of the first lecture and again at the very end of the module the following question:

"Who am I?"

Abstracts from the following selection student responses illustrate that there was a positive shift in developing emotional intelligence:

Student 'A': Who am I?
- Statement written at first lecture: *I am 20 years old. Currently in the second year of my maths degree. I am a football enthusiast. I eat, sleep, drink and think football.*
- Statement written at end of module: *I am a confident, motivated person. I'm not afraid to speak up when something affects my religious morals. I have realised that emotions are meant to be controlled, not blocked out. I have a better understanding of my inner emotions and how to cope with them.*

Student 'B': Who am I?
- Statement written at first lecture: *I'm (age), born and raised in (country). I speak French. I have been living in Manchester for almost 4 years.*
- Statement written at end of module: *I am easily distracted. I am a positive person, I am a friendly person who enjoys meeting new people. I take my university studies seriously.*

Student 'C': Who am I?
- Statement written at first lecture: *I am 21 years old. In the future I am wanting to be a maths teacher. I enjoy drawing and baking cakes, but don't have much time to enjoy these pleasures. I also enjoy doing exercise but only sport based.*
- Statement written at end of module: *Kind of torn between where I want to be in a few years, life is going too fast and I'm not ready to grow up. The responsibility commitment is a scary thought, but it's going to happen regardless of how I feel about*

it. I have a short attention span so I zone out a lot and try to get myself back in the room – especially in lectures.

Student 'D': Who am I?
- Statement written at first lecture: *Blue eyes. 6ft 1 in. Terribly dressed. Massive Man City fan. Good friend.*
- Statement written at end of module: *Confident – apparently cocky. Good listener. Love football. Know what I want to do in life. Like giving compliments. Like watching other people learn. Love family. Ambitious. Approachable.*

The above abstracts do evidence a shift in maturity and emotional intelligence – each student (statement) has shown a heightened level of self-awareness following the completion of the module, highlighting both strengths and areas of self-improvement for themselves. Each student has evidenced in their statements a deeper understanding of their inner self.

Anecdotally, Chadwick has reported a personal change in a majority of students following the completion of the module – of which some students have made significant steps forward in conquering fears such as speaking with more confidence in lectures, being more engaged in lectures, and students not being struck by exam anxiety.

SUMMARY

Teaching Emotional Intelligence in HEIs is still a fairly new area, particularly within the STEM subjects. It is highly likely that this is the first time an Emotional Intelligence module has been delivered within a taught Mathematics/STEM degree in the United Kingdom. This module impacts on student experience, both in terms of raising student employability skills, but perhaps more crucially, developing a skill set within students which will equip them for an increased quality of life and self-confidence, which ever career they choose to follow. One particular area for future development is to incorporate / encourage a diet rich in magnesium with a student cohort and / or exposing students to a magnesium foundry, such as Meridian Lightweight Technologies, and assess what difference this makes to their emotional intelligence.

Acknowledgements
The authors would like to acknowledge funding for the case study project from a CPD grant from the NWUA and National HESTEM Programme.

References
Castiglioni, S., Cazzaniga, A., Albisetti, W., & Maier, J. A. (2013). Magnesium and osteoporosis: current state of knowledge and future research directions. *Nutrients*, 5, (8), 3022-3033.
Chadwick, E., Sandiford K. and Percy, D. (2011). Assessing student teams developing mathematical models applied to business and industrial mathematics, *MSOR Connections*, 11, (3), 22–24.
Chadwick, E. and Radu O. (2012). Evaluating assessment practices in a business and industrial mathematics module. In:- Iannone, P. and Simpson, A. (eds). *University Assessment Practices*. University of East Anglia, 75–82.
Chadwick, E. and Singh, M. (eds.) (2012). Employer engagement: case studies for adoption in HE mathematical sciences. The National HE STEM Programme, University of Birmingham.
Cropley, D. and Cropley, A. (2005). Engineering creativity: a systems concept of functional creativity. In:- Kaufman, J. and Baer, J. Creativity across domains. London, Lawrence Erlbaum Associates. 169-185.
De Baaij, J. H., Hoenderop, J. G., & Bindels, R. J. (2015). Magnesium in man: implications for health and disease. *Physiological reviews*, 95, (1), 1-46.
Dong, J. Y., Xun, P., He, K., & Qin, L. Q. (2011). Magnesium intake and risk of type 2 diabetes. *Diabetes Care*, 34, (9), 2116-2122.

Downes, S. (2006, October 16). Learning networks and connective knowledge. Instructional Technology Forum: Paper 92. http://it.coe.uga.edu/itforum/paper92/paper92.html

Goleman, D. (1995). Emotional intelligence: why it can matter more than IQ. New York, NY: Bantam Books.

Hruby, A., O'Donnell, C. J., Jacques, P. F., Meigs, J. B., Hoffmann, U. & McKeown, N. M. (2014). Magnesium intake is inversely associated with coronary artery calcification: the Framingham heart study. *JACC: Cardiovascular Imaging*, 7, (1), 59-69.

Jenkins, H. (2006). Fans, bloggers, and gamers: Exploring participatory culture. NYU Press.

Kelly, K. (2016). The inevitable: understanding the 12 technological forces that will shape our future. 1st ed. New York: Penguin Random House LLC.

Kop, R. & Hill, A. (2008). Connectivism: learning theory of the future or vestige of the past? *The International Review of Research in Open and Distributed Learning*, 9, (3).

Maths Careers (2016). Graduates. [online] Available at: http://www.mathscareers.org.uk/ [Accessed 24 March 2016].

Oman, S. K., Tumer, I. Y., Wood, K. & Seepersad, C. (2013). A comparison of creativity and innovation metrics and sample validation through in-class design projects. *Research in Engineering Design*, 24, (1), 65-92.

Perls, F. (1973). *The Gestalt Approach & Eye Witness to Therapy*. New York: Bantam Books.

Petrides, K.V., Fredrickson, N. and Furnham, A. (2004). The role of trait emotional intelligence in academic performance and deviant behavior at school. *Personality and Individual Differences*, 36, 277–293, Available at: http://www.psychometriclab.com/admins/files/paid%20(2004)%20%20t_ei.pdf [Accessed: 24 March 2016].

Qualter, P., Gardner, K. and Whiteley, H. (2007). Emotional intelligence: review of research and educational implications. *Pastoral Care in Education*, 25, (1) 11-20. Available at: http://onlinelibrary.wiley.com/doi/10.1111/j.1468-0122.2007.00395.x/epdf [Accessed: 01 April 2016].

Sartori, S. B., Whittle, N., Hetzenauer, A. & Singewald, N. (2012). Magnesium deficiency induces anxiety and HPA axis dysregulation: modulation by therapeutic drug treatment. *Neuropharmacology*, 62, (1), 304-312.

Savoley, P. and Meyer, J.D. (1990). Emotional intelligence, imagination cognition and personality, 9, (3), 185-211. Available at: http://ica.sagepub.com/content/9/3/185 [Accessed: 24 March 2016].

Singh, M. (2000). The journey: where seagulls dare to fly. Leicester: Book Guild Publishing Ltd.

Singh, M. and Chadwick, E. (2015). Emotional intelligence in STEM, *Mathematics Today*, Institute of Mathematics and its Applications, 51, (2), 75-77.

Siemens, G. (2005, August 10). Connectivism: learning as network creation. e-Learning Space.org website. http://www.elearnspace.org/Articles/networks.htm

Slutsky, I., Abumaria, N., Wu, L. J., Huang, C., Zhang, L., Li, B., ... & Tonegawa, S. (2010). Enhancement of learning and memory by elevating brain magnesium. *Neuron*, 65, (2), 165-177.

Sternberg, R. (1988). The nature of creativity: contemporary psychological perspectives. New York, NY, Cambridge University Press.

Stewart, B. E. (2015). In abundance: networked participatory practices as scholarship. *The International Review of Research in Open and Distributed Learning*, 16, (3). http://www.irrodl.org/index.php/irrodl/article/view/2158/3343

Toland, A. (2011). *HE STEM Employability Skills Review*. [pdf] Birmingham: The National HE STEM Programme. Available at: http://www.hestem.ac.uk/sites/default/files/employability_skills_review.pdf [Accessed: 24 March 2016].

UKCES, (2010). *Skills for Jobs: Today and Tomorrow*. London: UKCES. Available at: https://www.gov.uk/government/publications/skills-for-jobs-today-and-tomorrow. [Accessed: 24 March 2016].

Waldock, J. and Rowlett, P. (eds.) (2012). *Employer Engagement in Undergraduate Mathematics*. [pdf] Birmingham: The National HE STEM Programme. Available at: http://www.mathcentre.ac.uk/resources/uploaded/EmployerEngagement.pdf [Accessed: 24 March 2016].

Supporting Women in Science and Engineering with BCU and Meridian Lightweight Technologies UK

Laura Leyland

School of Engineering and the Built Environment, Birmingham City University, Millennium Point, Birmingham, UK. B4 7AP.
Email: laura.leyland@bcu.ac.uk

Abstract

Well reported figures detail the lack of women in the engineering industry, for example, the Institute of Engineering Technology (IET) Skills Survey 2016 reported that women make up only nine percent of all engineering and technology employees (IET, 2016). Gender diversity remains a huge challenge for the sector, including that of the casting industries. Birmingham City University (BCU) and Meridian Lightweight Technologies UK (MLTUK) are working together to develop opportunities to support women as they enter this exciting world of engineering. At BCU, the engineering team are challenged with very low numbers of female undergraduates studying engineering courses, five percent, which falls below the sector mean. As a result, the team have recently undertaken a radical rewrite of our curriculum, taking the opportunity to widen the appeal of the courses which will be delivered from September 2017. To support female students and staff, BCU is an institutional member of Women in Science and Engineering (WISE) and we have a new WISE society. BCU was also recently awarded Athena Swan Bronze award which supports its journey towards a more balanced work force. Sponsored by MLTUK, the BCU engineering team have three student bursaries available. Potential students will be invited to apply, and the winning candidates will receive not only monetary support, but a valuable opportunity to spend a month working with Meridian in the summer at the end of the first year of study. This will be in place for students starting their courses in September 2017. This will not only benefit the team at BCU but will also benefit their colleagues at Meridian as they will be working with talented engineering students who will be undertaking project work. This will provide opportunities to promote the magnesium industry while working towards a more diverse workforce.

Keywords
Women, Bursary, WISE

INTRODUCTION

The challenging problem to increase the gender balance of the engineering sector, so called occupational segregation, is well documented. This chapter outlines the multi-faceted approach undertaken by BCU as it strives for more female representation. Beginning with outreach activities, the engineering team is working with schools to inform and inspire girls' future into Science, Technology, Engineering and Mathematics (STEM) starting from year eight, approximately age thirteen, before they take their options which set the career path.

In order to increase the profile of engineering courses to the female population, and to encourage more women to apply, the engineering team is working with MLTUK to offer bursaries to women who apply to engineering courses at BCU. This will give both monetary reward and opportunity for work experience during an internship at the end of their first year of study. Engineering courses have been rewritten to be more attractive and applicable to a more diverse student body. Once the team has succeeded in attracting women onto their courses, undergraduate and postgraduate, support for this minority group is provided through the Women in Science and Engineering (WISE) society which offers a range of events, mentoring opportunities and support. At an institutional level, BCU has been looking carefully at gender representation, and have just been awarded the Athena Swan bronze award as the first step on this journey.

OUTREACH

Inspiring the next generation, and dispelling the traditional image of engineers. Therefore, the team at BCU will be working with students before they take their GCSE options which put them on a career path. For example, International Women in Engineering Day where we invite eighty, Year Eight, students from eight local schools to join us for the day. The students hear from women from different branches of the engineering and the built environment sector about their roles and how they got there. The team will have the students working in small groups of five with a mentor. The mentors are supporters from industry and academics who work with the teams, having real conversations about their roles and breaking down barriers. The challenge the girls work on have been developed from Practical Actions STEM challenges written for schools (Brown, 2017). This year the BCU team focussed on creating hand washing devices for a school in Kenya which use a restricted amount of water. Importantly, the students also had to communicate how the device works and why it's needed, as a clear message for the Kenyan school children so they can take the message home. The girls are so inspiring, every team managed to create a working model. Feedback from the day clearly demonstrates that the girls enjoy working creatively and constructively in teams to solve real problems: "The best day of my life" reported one of the girls. They clearly enjoy engineering.

NEW, MORE APPEALING COURSES

At BCU the team are challenged with very low numbers of female undergraduates studying the engineering courses, which falls below the sector mean, see Figure 1.

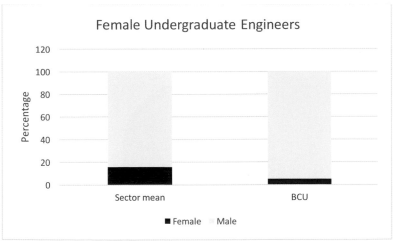

FIGURE 1: Number of female undergraduates studying engineering courses.

Therefore, the team and university recently undertaken a radical rewrite of our curriculum, taking the opportunity to widen the appeal of our courses which will be delivered from September 2017. The main highlights of the new engineering courses are the common first year for the six engineering programmes: Mechanical; Automotive; Civil; Electronics;

Manufacturing; and, Biomedical. Students will all be involved in interdisciplinary project work, solving real problems from the very first week of their studies. The curriculum is following the Conceive-Design-Implement-Operate (CDIO) framework. This supports the assimilation of technical knowledge alongside professional skills including teamwork, leadership and project management as students work together to build a solution, which are all vital skills for engineering graduates. See Yusof (2016) and Crawley *et al.* (2014).

SUPPORT FROM INDUSTRY

Sponsored by MLTUK the team at BCU have three student bursaries available as a pilot project for the 2017 academic year. The aim of these bursaries is to encourage more women to apply for engineering courses. Potential students will be invited to submit a short piece of work, the winning candidates will receive not only monetary support, but a valuable opportunity to spend a month working with MLTUK in the summer at the end of the first year of study. We are inviting other companies to widen this opportunity. It is anticipated that the team at BCU might have a group of companies, representing the professions relating to Engineering and the Built Environment willing to support this activity, so that the team at BCU might have a range of bursaries and internships to offer going forward. The long-range goal, is that as BCU will get closer to parity, these will become available to all students. The opportunities for MLTUK as they partner with us for this project is that they have access to talented engineering students to undertake project work alongside opportunities to promote the magnesium industry while working towards a more diverse workforce.

SUPPORT STUDENTS AND STAFF

The current number of women on engineering courses at BCU are very low, but those that are there are likely to achieve a first class, upper second-class degree classification, see Figure 2, or they leave. Figure 3 represents the same data for the male cohort for comparison. It's important that those students are supported by the team at BCU, especially if they start to struggle with any element of the course.

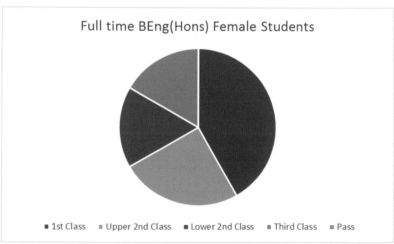

FIGURE 2: Degree classification of female undergraduates studying engineering courses registering between 2001 and 2010.

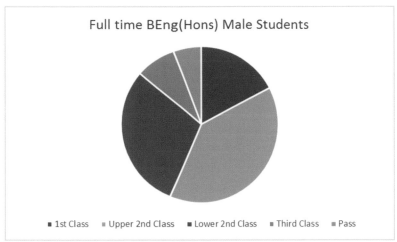

FIGURE 3: Degree classification of male undergraduates studying engineering courses registering between 2001 and 2010.

To support students, and staff, BCU is an institutional member of Women in Science and Engineering (WISE) which gives us access to a regional hub of activity and support, and resources to support our new WISE society. The society provides events, both social and business, mentoring opportunities, access to conferences and networking events for staff and students.

Athena Swan is a programme dedicated to recognising the advancement of gender equality: representation, progression and success for all in the higher education sector. BCU has been awarded Athena Swan Bronze award, which supports our journey towards a more balanced work force.

CONCLUSIONS

The events run to support International Women in Engineering Day have now been running for three years, with the first cohort taking their GCSE exams this summer. It is anticipated that engineering at BCU should start to see some of the fruits of this work with applications over the next two years. Currently, there are projects underway with undergraduate students interviewing engineers and scientists, creating case-studies and materials for our marketing outlets. We need to tell the story of the work that is underway.

There is no panacea to the low numbers of women in the engineering sector, a multi-faceted approach is being used with schools and industry whilst looking within at the way in which the team at BCU is able to deliver and support both students and staff as they move forward to a more gender balanced future.

Acknowledgements
The author would like to thank Meridian Lightweight Technologies UK for financial support to create this pilot project enabling the WISE bursaries. The views expressed in this paper are those of the author and do not necessarily represent those of Meridian Lightweight Technologies UK.

References
Brown, J. (2017) Stop the Spread. Practical Action. Available online https://practicalaction.org/stem

Crawley E, Malmqvist, J, Ostlund, S, Brodeur, D, Edstrom, K (2014). Rethinking Engineering Education. Springer. Second Edition.

Institute of Engineering Technology (2016) Skills and Demand in Industry Survey, (IET).

Yusof *et al.*, (2016). Instilling professional skills and sustainable development through Problem Based Learning (PBL) among first year engineering students. *International Journal of Engineering Education*, 32, [1], 333-347

Attitudes Towards the Use of Magnesium Alloys by Engineers

Panagiotis Rentzelas and Eirini Mavritsaki

School of Business, Law and Social Sciences, Department of Psychology Birmingham City University, 4 Cardigan Street, Birmingham, UK. B4 7BD.
Email: panagiotis.rentzelas@bcu.ac.uk and eirini.mavritsaki@bcu.ac.uk

Abstract

The purpose of this paper is to provide an outline how engineer's attitudes over magnesium alloys can be empirically investigated using psychological theory and research. This will be achieved by providing an overview of key theories in attitude formation and change and how individual differences psychological constructs can moderate attitude formation over magnesium alloys. More specifically this chapter will investigate how previous psychological research on adaptation of new technology can adapted and informed our empirical approach.

Keywords

Attitudes, Theory of Planned Behaviour, Theory of Reasoned Action, Technology Adaptation

INTRODUCTION

In this chapter, we will not try to go over the benefits of the use of magnesium based alloys on the automotive and aerospace industries (or indeed to any other industries where magnesium alloys can be utilised). This chapter is an additional contribution to the one that our colleagues with an engineering background explore in their chapters. In our chapter, we will like to investigate how automotive and aerospace industries based engineers formulate attitudes and risks perception on the use of magnesium based alloy. This will be achieved by providing a short review of the psychological theory and research in the area of attitude formation and risk perception and by proposing an empirical research plan.

REVIEW OF PSYCHOLOGICAL THEORY

It should be noted that the engineer's attitudes towards magnesium alloys have not been assessed before and anecdotal evidence from the industry suggest that engineers might be reluctant using magnesium related products. In order to address this gap in the literature we are proposing a scoping pilot study on the engineer's attitudes that will be conducted following the methodology of previous research (Edison & Geisler, 2003) where attitudes towards new technology and brand names was investigated. Furthermore, we will investigate the psychological constructs for need for cognition (Cacioppo & Petty 1982) as well as measurements for affinity for technology (Parasuraman 2000), tolerance for ambiguity (Stanley Budner 1962) and locus of control (Rotter 1966). Previous research suggests that locus of control correlates negatively towards attitudes to use new technology whereas locus of control and affinity for technology positively (Cacioppo & Petty 1982).

Attitudes are the personal beliefs that an individual holds over a target behaviour or object and they can be negative or positive. There is a plethora of psychological research that examined how attitudes are formulated, empirically measured and how they can be used in order to predict an individual's behaviour (Armitage & Christian 2003). Attitudes are powerful psychological constructs that have been used excessively by psychologists and other social scientists in order to empirically investigate how individuals formulate certain behavioural patterns towards attitude objects ranging all the way from exercise and safe sex to the adaptation of new technology (Edison & Geissler 2003), consumption of genetically modified food (Spence & Townsend 2006) all the way to the geoengineering (Pidgeon *et al.* 2012). For the purpose of this project, we are proposing that the best attitude theoretical approach is the framework of the Theory of Planned Behaviour and Theory of Reasoned Action (Ajzen 1991; Fishbein & Ajzen 1975). These theories postulate that the link between an attitude and behaviour can be better understood – and more importantly increase the predictive validity of attitudes over behaviour - if also other constructs are considered as well. For example, intentions over a target object, in this case magnesium alloys. An intention is a motivational construct that reflects the extent of an individual's readiness, planning and effort to engage in a particular behaviour. Another important construct is perceived behavioural control which refers to the perceptions that an individual holds over a target behaviour and the degree that a targeted behaviour is evaluated positively or negatively. The above described theoretical framework can be used in such a way where the psychological components of an attitude (*i.e.* intentions and perceived behavioural control) can be utilised to understand how behaviours towards magnesium alloys are being formulated.

Previous research in the area of attitudes towards technology (Edison & Geissler 2003) suggest that apart of the above described Theory of Planned Behaviour and Theory of Reasoned Action constructs also additional psychological and individual differences constructs should be taken under consideration when we examine – especially – the formation of attitudes towards new technology. For example, Locus of Control (Rotter 1966) refers to a psychological individual differences trait where an individual believes that is in control of his or her actions. Locus of control is a psychological trait that should be perceived as continuum where individuals that high internal control tend to feel that more in control of their environment. Engineers that score high in a scale measuring locus of control could be more prone to use magnesium based alloys, as such individuals tend to be better on assessing new information and more willing to change already established behaviours and attitudes.

Like locus of control in this line of research we will be also considering measuring other psychological traits like need for cognition and tolerance of ambiguity. Need of cognition refers to psychological trait where an individual actually enjoys thinking (Cacioppo & Petty 1982). Individuals with high levels of need for cognition prefer more complex tasks and are better on adapting new technology (Edinonson & Geissler 2003). Furthermore, tolerance to ambiguity refers the tendency that some individuals have to ambiguous situations as desirable and trying to make the most of them. Individuals that indicate high levels of ambiguity tolerance are more likely to adapt new technology than individuals who indicate low levels. In line with the background literature, we expect that engineers who are more autonomous and feel to higher control over the environment, appreciate thinking and complex situations and are open to ambiguity will indicate to be more prone to adapt magnesium alloys.

In this line of research, we are willing to adopt established and replicated psychological research in order to investigate how automotive and aerospace engineers formulate attitudes towards the use of magnesium alloys. The psychological constructs described above will be empirically measured by the use of validated questionnaires and psychometric tools. Apart from an explicit investigation of attitudes, impolite measurements will also be employed as they are less influences by external factors (Rosenberg, 1969) or demand characteristics (Orne 1962).

References

Ajzen, I. (1991). The Theory of Planned Behavior. *Organizational Behavior and Human Decision Processes,* 50, (2), 179-211.

Armitage, C.J. & Christian, J. (2003). From Attitudes to Behaviour: Basic and Applied Research on the Theory of Planned Behaviour. *Current Psychology,* 22, (3), pp.187–195. Available at: http://www.springerlink.com/index/T3Y0T9Q7E3HNJN4H.pdf\npapers2://publication/uuid/C8F700D4-836B-454D-962B-2EFBF8E87C9D .

Cacioppo, J.T. & Petty, R.E. (1982). The need for cognition. *Journal of Personality and Social Psychology,* 42, (1), 116–131. Available at: http://content.apa.org/journals/psp/42/1/116 .

Edison, S.W. & Geissler, G.L. (2003). Measuring attitudes towards general technology: Antecedents, hypotheses and scale development. *Journal of Targeting, Measurement and Analysis for Marketing,* 12, (2), 137–156.

Fishbein, M., & Ajzen, I. (1975). *Belief, attitude, intention, and behavior: An introduction to theory and research.* Reading, M: Addison-Wesley.

Orne, M., (1962). On the social psychology of the psychological experiment. *American Psychologist,* 17, 776–783.

Parasuraman, A. (2000). Technology readiness index (Tri). *Journal of Service Research,* 2, (4), 307–320. Available at: http://dx.doi.org/10.1177/109467050024001 .

Pidgeon, N. *et al.* (2012). Exploring early public responses to geoengineering. *Philosophical Transactions of the Royal Society A: Mathematical, Physical and Engineering Sciences,* 370, (1974), 4176–4196. Available at: http://rsta.royalsocietypublishing.org/cgi/doi/10.1098/rsta.2012.0099.

Rosenberg, M., J. (1969). The conditions and consequences of evaluation apprehension. In R. Rosenthal and R. L. Rosnow (eds.). Artefact in Behavioural Research. New York: Academic Press.

Rotter, J.B. (1966). Generalized expectancies for internal versus external control of reinforcement. *Psychological Monographs: General and Applied,* 80, (1), 1–28. Available at: http://doi.apa.org/getdoi.cfm?doi=10.1037/h0092976 .

Spence, A. & Townsend, E. (2006). Implicit attitudes towards genetically modified (GM) foods: A comparison of context-free and context-dependent evaluations. *Appetite,* 46, (1), 67–74.

Stanley Budner, N.Y. (1962). Intolerance of ambiguity as a personality variable1. *Journal of Personality,* 30, (1), 29–50. Available at: http://dx.doi.org/10.1111/j.1467-6494.1962.tb02303.x.

What it Means to Innovate: Vulnerabilities and Risks

Clayton Shaw

STEAMhouse, Institute of Creative Innovation, Research, Innovation & Enterprise,
Birmingham City University, University House, Birmingham, UK. B5 5JU.
Email: clayton.shaw@bcu.ac.uk

Abstract

In this chapter, the author provides an insight into the process of collaborative open innovation and the challenge it can present to its participants. It covers the way that participation in team based open collaboration formats can benefit from deconstructing their product ideas, and in doing so requires participants to relinquish direct control. It is illustrated through the emerging relationship between an artist and an advanced manufacturing company, and through the author's personal account of past innovation techniques that used similar methodologies. There is reference to the acronym STEAM (Science, Engineering, Technology, Arts and Maths), and how the combination of associated disciplines can layer new perspectives over problems to find new solutions.

Keywords
Innovation, Collaboration, Vulnerability.

INTRODUCTION

Over the past few months, since work started on the Birmingham City University (BCU) led STEAMhouse project, there has been an overwhelming interest in the desire for people inside and outside the organisation to connect with people from other disciplines, and to openly collaborate, share, and receive new knowledge and ideas. Innovation is what people are seeking, and they are exploring it in new ways.

It is still early days in the lifespan of BCU's mission to encourage the development of a hyper-connected, mobile, and creative community of active thinkers and doers; unafraid of taking sometimes pioneering steps into unknown and unfamiliar territory. What does it mean to be able to achieve this, and why would anyone be tempted to step so far outside of their comfort zones?

INNOVATION AND VULNERABILITY

Placing oneself in a vulnerable position is something most would want to avoid or at least steer clear. It is not easy, nor is it a regular pursuit of choice, but perhaps it is something that can be learned, appreciated, and valued. Deconstructing the uncertainties to the basics, and constructing building blocks through the process of cross-disciplinary working can, and does provide numerous rewards from the most unexpected of corners. For example, at the inaugural *STEAMlab* (a group based multidisciplinary open innovation workshop) in March 2017, an unexpected but potentially beneficial relationship was initiated between artist Harmeet Chagger-Khan and Meridian, an advanced manufacturing company working in innovative lightweight cast metal solutions for the transportation industry.

Meridian was an ideal organisation to partner with as the staff were willing to engage with arts and creative industry professionals, normally outside of their sphere of work. This is probably in part due to the organisation's vision to be at the leading edge of what they do.

To reiterate, new-found collaboration opportunity between global advanced manufacturing company and artist was only made possible as the participants maintained an open minded, curious approach to explore a new concept. Should the partnership continue, further down the line other issues will undoubtedly emerge, *i.e.* those of trust, relationship management, roles and responsibilities, IP, and finance, again, raising new vulnerabilities as the participants enter on a journey of unknown results. Nevertheless, the opportunity exists, and should the participants apply the same open approach, great things could be achieved.

The immediate result of the newly formed relationship is that Chagger-Khan is now working on addressing the negative perceptions of the properties of magnesium – that it is highly combustible and dangerous – perceptions derived from school class room chemistry experiments. Unfortunately, this seems to be a broadly accepted and firmly embedded perception among many people which Meridian will need to address if it is to enter new markets, particularly one as safety conscious as the aerospace industry. Those in the magnesium industry recognise that the metal's properties are in complete contrast to these perceptions, that it is indeed lightweight, strong, and safe. Chagger-Khan is now working to deconstruct the ill-placed perceptions through an artistic solution.

The lab provided a space to iterate on a process that identified problem, solution, problem, solution, problem until the ideal solution emerged to best demonstrate the metal's properties. The artist is now working on prototyping a kite based kinetic structure or sculpture. This solution could provide a unique starting point for Meridian to enter a dialogue with players in the aerospace industry, moving beyond standard modes of presentation, and working in a way more consistent with an organisation that seeks to lead, innovate with technology, and find remarkable and inspiring ways of telling their story. Furthermore, it opens a new door for the artist to work in an industry which would otherwise have remained outside of their usual network, and opening up new avenues to create novel work.

It is accepted that this approach will not appeal to every artist who may wish to retain complete and unfettered artistic control over their work, but to others it presents new opportunities to be creative within a new context which can both challenge and cultivate professional advancement. Similarly, not all industries would immediately recognise the return on investment benefits by taking this approach, as it presents an element of risk, however, the opportunities can be attractive if viewed through an alternative, creative, lens.

INNOVATION AND RISK

We must accept that there will not be quick wins for everyone. This is the risk, or gamble, we take when entering such creative and multifaceted environments. From personal experience, the pursuit to innovating practices does not always bring the desired result. Back in 2013 while working for the arts organisation, Sampad, the author worked in collaboration with a digital company, Mixed Reality Studio, as part of the University of Birmingham's *Collaborative Arts Triple Helix* project, set up to establish cross-disciplinary research partnerships to develop a new augmented reality game called A*GILE (Arts Gaming for Interactive Learning and Engagement)* to engage young people in arts and culture. The idea seemed fairly simple - to create an augmented reality app whereby users could locate animated characters within real world settings, with points awarded for the most characters collected.

It sounds familiar now since *Pokémon Go* rose to glory a few years later, but at the time we were not aware of anything like it. We had the concept, but not the investment despite numerous attempts from various sources to acquire it. The author is not saying that we could have achieved what Pokémon Go achieved (which, incidentally, was the result of a collaboration between Niantic and Nintendo), but it is interesting how we had hit on a similar idea but failed to be able to develop it beyond an early concept. Perhaps we sought the wrong type of investors, perhaps it was too 'out there' as a concept for the investors to grasp hold of at the time and they were unwilling to take a 'punt'. The fact remains that sometimes the investment in time, money, and energy we make to innovate will not always pay off, despite the strength of the idea for a variety of reasons, but this is the game we are motivated to play. Nevertheless, by accepting that not all collaborations will always be immediately fruitful we can to some extent remove the pressure to find an immediate solution, and create an environment to aid potentially new and unforeseen outcomes.

STEAMHOUSE METHODOLOGIES

Kelly (2016) describes a move toward a *"digital social-ism uniquely tuned for a networked world"*. He illustrates media theorist Clay Shirky's hierarchy on how the networked web is socialised, from sharing, to co-operation towards a shared goal, then collaboration on things such as open source software projects, and finally collectivism – a decentralised yet connected community of individuals uniting to "maximise both the autonomy of the individual and the power of people working together".

This echoes the nature of STEAMhouse which seeks to move away from a linear form of innovation based on singular disciplines working together to solve a problem to find a solution, and a move towards a collective multidisciplinary team of people coalescing around a problem to find multiple solutions, Figure 1.

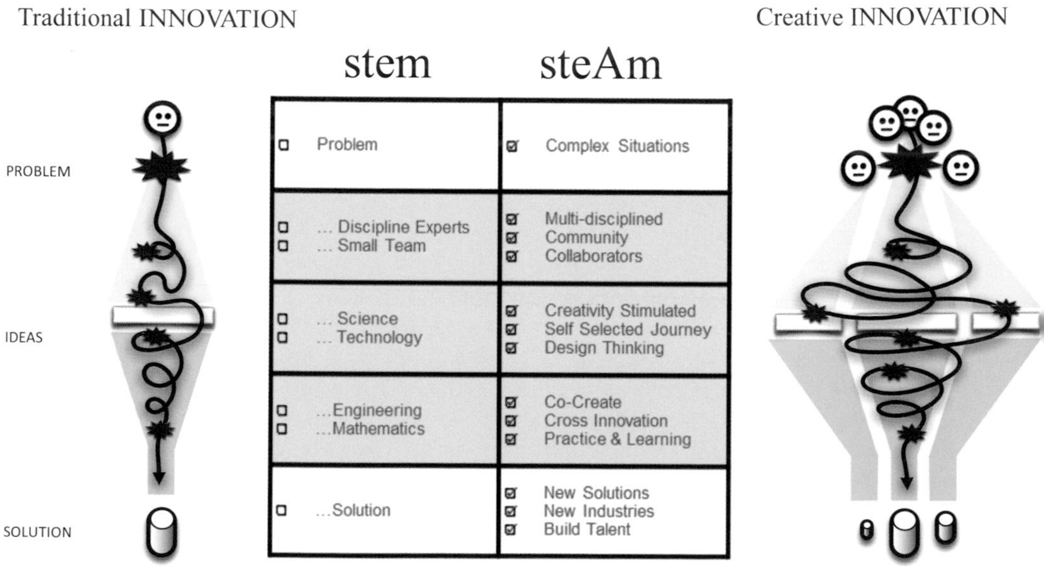

	stem		steAm	
PROBLEM	☐	Problem	☑	Complex Situations
	☐ ☐	... Discipline Experts ... Small Team	☑ ☑ ☑	Multi-disciplined Community Collaborators
IDEAS	☐ ☐	... Science ... Technology	☑ ☑ ☑	Creativity Stimulated Self Selected Journey Design Thinking
	☐ ☐	...Engineering ...Mathematics	☑ ☑ ☑	Co-Create Cross Innovation Practice & Learning
SOLUTION	☐	...Solution	☑ ☑ ☑	New Solutions New Industries Build Talent

Traditional INNOVATION   Creative INNOVATION

FIGURE 1: Illustration comparing traditional innovation and creative open innovation.

The underpinning approaches focus on STEAM activity being both interdisciplinary and transdisciplinary: Interdisciplinary - identifying a problem at the centre which allows each discipline to come up with the solution to fix it, and Trans-disciplinary - looking at developing methodologies where there is a concern which applies to both sets of disciplines but which, when reviewed together, create a third way to solve a problem.

CONCLUSION

The team at BCU have had, and will continue to have plenty of discussions about what STEAMhouse could and should be, particularly given the nature of the associated vulnerabilities around the process of collaboration. The aim is to provide a reassuring place for people to be open to share and receive ideas and new ways of thinking, to be curious and inquisitive, and to be inventive and unafraid to test, mould, and create. It also aims to encourage multiple viewpoints to break through new ideas, find new solutions to challenges, and to innovate and prototype in a very hands-on way. Interactions with others can also lead to developing a network of long lasting creative and collaborative relationships to further discuss, share, and develop new ideas into the future.

The approach seeks to imagine how people can engage with the challenges and opportunities around collaborative open innovation methodologies. It will form a community of likeminded individuals to break down silos, accept the associated vulnerabilities, find new networks, and reframe what it means to innovate in the digital age.

References
Kelly, K. (2016). *The Inevitable: Understanding the 12 Technological Forces that Will Shape Our Future*. 1st ed. New York: Penguin Random House LLC.
University of Birmingham (2014). *The Collaborative Arts Triple Helix project*. [ONLINE] Available at: http://www.birmingham.ac.uk/facilities/prototypinghall/projects/cath-project.aspx. [Accessed 27 June 2017].

Magnesium and Mobility: Investigating the Metal's Potential Role in a Low-Carbon Transport Industry

Michaela Rose

Forum for the Future, Overseas House, 19-23 Ironmonger Row, London, EC1V 3QN.
Email: M.Rose@forumforthefuture.org

Abstract

As a lightweight, strong and extremely recyclable material, magnesium offers the potential to lower the fuel emissions associated with the automotive, aviation and other industries. However, there remains several barriers and risks to using the metal at scale. This chapter explores the opportunities and challenges presented by magnesium, and looks at how a number of trends, including resource shortages, climate change and the rise of the circular economy, may influence its future and increase its value proposition. It concludes that if magnesium is to contribute significantly towards sustainability then ensuring safety, recyclability and low carbon manufacturing processes is key.

Keywords
Circular Economy, Mobility, Decarbonisation

INTRODUCTION

The transport industry is responsible for approximately 23% of total energy-related CO_2 emissions, and this looks set to nearly double by 2050 without "aggressive and sustained" mitigation policies being implemented (Sims and Schaeffer, 2014). If the world is to meet the Paris Agreement's core objective of keeping global warming well below 2°C, every industry is going to have to play its part through radical decarbonisation.

While engineers look for increasingly low-impact mobility solutions to power and control our cars, ships, planes and trains, there remains considerable scope for finding better ways to build these vehicles, starting with materials. To cut fuel use, and thereby carbon emissions, developing means to reduce overall weight through material choice, while maintaining safety and performance, is a priority. Today, most planes and many trains are made from aluminium, while cars are typically made using a wide variety of materials, including steel, aluminium and numerous plastics, often as composites.

As a lightweight, strong, highly recyclable and extremely abundant material, magnesium holds a lot of promise, but has historically been largely underused by the transport industries, in part due to fears over its flammability and corrosiveness. Although the use of magnesium in cars, for example, is increasing by around 15% per year, the metal still makes up a very small part of the overall mix (Gándara, 2011). This chapter investigates the opportunities for magnesium to become a major component in vehicle design and a driver of the circular economy, and explores some the key challenges to using the metal at scale.

POWERFUL PROPERTIES AND THEIR PITFALLS

Abundance

Magnesium is the third most abundant metal found in the Earth's crust, and makes up 0.13 of seawater in the form of magnesium chloride. Despite its ample availability, the element is very rarely found naturally in its pure form, due to the fact that it bonds so easily with other elements (Intlmag.org, n.d.). Processes to extract magnesium from these compounds are typically highly energy intensive, and - depending on the primary energy source - responsible for high levels of greenhouse gas (GHG) emissions. The Pidgeon process is the most commonly used method due largely to comparatively low capital costs, but has low productivity and high energy consumption.

Recyclability and the Circular Economy
Magnesium is highly recyclable, and the process typically results in a 90% reduction of GHG emissions and energy usage compared with producing the primary material (IMA, 2017). However, since magnesium is most commonly used for structural processes as an alloy, there are additional complications to recycling, and processes involving distillation or re-melting of these alloys remain expensive (IMA, 2017). Despite some progress, further improvements are needed to establish an effective and low-cost recycling process. Furthermore, in the pursuit of "light weighting", the use of composite materials and glues in the production process are increasing, making recycling even more difficult and presenting a significant barrier to the circular economy for the automotive and aerospace industries generally.

Lightweight, but Strong
Magnesium is the lightest useful metal for structural applications, with a density of 1.7 g/cm^3, making it 33% lighter than aluminium and 75% lighter than steel. Despite its lower density, however, magnesium alloys have a comparable strength-to-weight ratio as aluminium (IMA, 2017). Therefore, the hope is that incorporating more magnesium alloys into vehicle manufacturing may offer the potential of lowering overall weight, thereby increasing fuel efficiencies and reducing GHG emissions.

Flammability and Corrosiveness
Although once widely used in the making of planes, the prevalence of magnesium declined in the 1970s due to increasing engine power and concerns over corrosion and flammability (Alderman, 2016), which have given the metal a 'bad name'. The recent lifting of a ban on the use of magnesium in plane seats may help pave the way for its increased use in aircraft design, and improve its image within transport industries.

SIGNALS OF CHANGE: TRENDS THAT MAY INFLUENCE MAGNESIUM'S FUTURE

Staying Within 1.5 °C
The minimum target outlined in the 2015 Paris Agreement was to limit the increase in the global average temperature to well below 2°C above pre-industrial levels and pursue efforts to limit the temperature increase to 1.5°C (Unfccc.int, n.d.). McSweeney and Pearce, (2016) estimate that to stand a 66% chance of staying below 1.5 °C, the world has little over four years of current emissions to use up the Intergovernmental Panel on Climate Change's (IPCC) carbon budgets. To meet the 1.5 °C target therefore requires the rapid and complete transformation of the global energy, transportation and agricultural systems. This means completely reshaping the operating context for all companies, and facing up to volatile and disruptive times ahead. As a very lightweight metal, magnesium could have a role to play in reducing fuel use in the highly polluting transport sector and therefore help the industry to decarbonise. However, for a radical and adequate transformation of the transport system, other radical solutions will also be required.

Green China

The rapid industrialisation of China has for a long time been centred on fossil fuel power generation, but is now rapidly shifting to more sustainable means. This includes an unprecedented investment in renewable energy, a new Emissions Trading Scheme and an extremely progressive five-year governmental plan to double wind energy capacity, triple solar (Tianjie, 2017), and increase the number of electric vehicles by a factor of five (Sanderson, Hancock and Lewis, 2017). As one of the world's largest producers of magnesium (IMA, 2017), China's shift to clean tech could see production methods fuelled entirely by zero-carbon sources, which would have profound sustainability implications for the metal.

Energy Transformation

The world is seeing a radical shift away from fossil fuel power generation in favour of renewables and other clean tech. Investments in oil and gas, for example, declined by an unprecedented 25% in 2015, while energy produced from renewables rose by more than 30% (Cooke, 2016). In addition, coal production in the U.S. has plummeted to its lowest level in 35 years (Park, 2016), with a corresponding drop in the costs of wind and solar power (Carrington, 2017). The IPCC (2011) predicts that nearly 80% of the World's energy supply could be met by renewables by mid-century if backed by the right public policies. Manufacturing magnesium is an energy-intensive process, and so any growth potential for the metal will be dependent on manufacturers being able to produce and recycle it using renewable energy as the primary source.

Lightweight Mobility

Manufacturers are increasingly using a mix of lightweight materials and plastic composites to reduce fuel reduction and increase automotive safety (Alderman, 2016). However, these mixes are harder or nearly impossible to separate, making the recyclability of the constituent parts and their role in a circular economy next to zero, but there remains considerable scope for "light-weighting". Bautista (2017) found that reducing automotive weight using aluminium can help save 65 litres of fuel per car per year. Magnesium is 33% lighter than aluminium, meaning there are potentially even greater savings to be made by incorporating more of it into vehicle design.

Resource Shortages

Based on current consumption habits, 1.6 planets would be needed to support humanity's demand on the Earth's ecosystem (WWF, 2016). Fears over materials security are driving governments' and companies' strategic decisions, with more than a half of businesses anticipating their companies' core business objectives to be affected by natural resource shortages (e.g., water, energy, forest products, rare earth minerals/metals) in the next three to five years (Ey.com, n.d.). By being the fourth most common element in the Earth, magnesium's abundance will be appealing for manufacturers seeking security of supply. However, it is still a finite resource and circular material loops remain key to making this a sustainable material source.

Circular Economy

"In a circular economy, growth is decoupled from the use of scarce resources through disruptive technology and business models based on longevity, renewability, reuse, repair, upgrade, refurbishment, capacity sharing, and dematerialization" (Accenture 2014). According to Lacy and Rutqvist (2015), even in spite of the transition costs, if a circular economy could be achieved in the EU by 2030 it could unlock $4.5 trillion in economic

growth by 2030 and up to $25 trillion by 2050. Magnesium recycling processes have already been embedded for scrap from production as well as postconsumer scrap. However, more circular models are required to make magnesium a closed-loop industry and as already shown above (see Lightweight Mobility), the increased use of mixed materials and plastic composites to make vehicles lighter are creating their own unique challenge for recycling and the circular economy.

A TOOLKIT FOR CIRCULARITY

In partnership with Unilever, Forum for the Future has developed a Circular Business Model toolkit identifying 10 circular business model archetypes, which distil long-term research into circular business models and include case studies (Forumforthefuture.org, n.d.). Several of these archetypes can be applied to magnesium:

- Closed-loop recycling: using recycled products as raw materials to manufacture new products.
  Case study: Jaguar XE's REALCAR project.
- Down-cycling: Turning materials from one or more used products into a new product with lower quality.
  Case study: Renault's Choisy-le-Roi factory.
- Up-cycling: Turning materials from one or more used products into a new product, implying an improvement in quality.
  Case study: Toyota Global 100 Dismantlers project.
- Industrial symbiosis: Sharing services, utilities and by-products among industries to improve resource efficiency.
  Case study: Timberland Tires.
- Local loop: As production processes are re-shored back into the countries where the business has its main markets, the local manufacturing loop becomes closer and benefits clustering of industries.
  Case study: Tesla's Gigafactory in co-operation with Panasonic and other strategic partners.
- Modularity: A design that divides a product into smaller parts that can then be independently created, used and replaced.
  Case study: Polyscope's Claut.
- Product and services: Consumer offers that put the focus on providing a solution rather than a product only. This leads to a marketable set of joint products and services that are capable of fulfilling a user's needs together.
  Case study: DriveNow programme.

CONCLUSION

Growing concerns over resource shortages and climate change, combined with the gradual "greenification" of China, the rise of the circular economy and a global renewable energy revolution, may all serve to increase the value proposition of magnesium's use in transportation. As an extremely abundant, lightweight, strong and particularly recyclable material, magnesium offers the potential to lessen the environmental impacts of the highly polluting car and aviation industries, but despite the metal's numerous positive attributes, there are several barriers to using the metal at scale. If magnesium is to contribute significantly to a sustainable future, then ensuring safety, recyclability and low carbon manufacturing processes are key.

Bibliography

Accenture (2014). *Circular Advantage: Innovative Business Models and Technologies to Create Value in a World without Limits to Growth.* [Online]. USA: Accenture Strategy. Available at: https://www.accenture.com/t20150523T053139__w__/us-en/_acnmedia/Accenture/Conversion-Assets/DotCom/Documents/Global/PDF/Strategy_6/Accenture-Circular-Advantage-Innovative-Business-Models-Technologies-Value-Growth.pdf [Accessed 18 Jul. 2017].

Alderman, M. (2016). 'A Perspective: Potential Growth in the Global Magnesium Industry — Where is Our Research Leading Us?' *Magnesium Technology.* pp.59-60.

Bautista, R. (2017). *Auto-loop: Driving in circles with vehicle recycling | Forum for the Future.* [Online]. Forumforthefuture.org. Available at: https://www.forumforthefuture.org/blog/auto-loop-driving-circles-with-vehicle-recycling [Accessed 18 Jul. 2017].

Carrington, D. (2017). ''Spectacular' drop in renewable energy costs leads to record global boost.' *The Guardian.* [Online]. Available at: https://www.theguardian.com/environment/2017/jun/06/spectacular-drop-in-renewable-energy-costs-leads-to-record-global-boost [Accessed 18 Jul. 2017].

Cooke, K. (2016). 'IEA: oil, gas investments fell 25% in 2015.' *Climate Home.* [Online]. Available at: http://www.climatechangenews.com/2016/09/23/iea-oil-gas-investments-fell-25-in-2015./ [Accessed 18 Jul. 2017].

Ey.com. (n.d.). *Increased risk and proximity of natural resource shortages.* [Online]. Available at: http://www.ey.com/us/en/services/specialty-services/climate-change-and-sustainability-services/increased-risk-and-proximity-of-natural-resource-shortages [Accessed 18 Jul. 2017].

Forumforthefuture.org. (n.d.). *The Circular Economy Business Model Toolkit | Forum for the Future.* [Online] Available at: https://www.forumforthefuture.org/project/circular-economy-business-model-toolkit/overview [Accessed 18 Jul. 2017].

Gándara, M. (2011). Recent Growing Demand For Magnesium in the Automotive Industry. *Materials and technology.* [Online]. 45(6), pp.633-637. Available at: http://mit.imt.si/Revija/izvodi/mit116/gandara.pdf [Accessed 18 Jul. 2017].

Intergovernmental Panel on Climate Change. (2011). *Potential of Renewable Energy Outlined in Report by the Intergovernmental Panel on Climate Change.* [Online]. Available at: http://www.ipcc.ch/news_and_events/docs/ipcc33/IPCC_Press_Release_11612_en.pdf [Accessed 18 Jul. 2017].

Intlmag.org. (n.d.). *About Magnesium - International Magnesium Association.* [Online]. Available at: http://www.intlmag.org/page/basics_about_mg_ima [Accessed 18 Jul. 2017].

Intlmag.org. (n.d.). *Lifecycle Analysis - International Magnesium Association.* [Online]. Available at: http://www.intlmag.org/page/sustain_life_ima [Accessed 18 Jul. 2017].

Lacy, P. and Rutqvist, J. (2015). *Waste to Wealth.* Basingstoke, ZULU: Palgrave Macmillan.

McRae, L. (2016). *Living Planet Report 2016.* World Wildlife Fund Canada.

McSweeney, R. and Pearce, R. (2016). *Analysis: Only five years left before 1.5C carbon budget is blown | Carbon Brief.* [Online]. Carbon Brief. Available at: http://www.carbonbrief.org/analysis-only-five-years-left-before-one-point-five-c-budget-is-blown. [Accessed 18 Jul. 2017].

Park, B. (2016). *Quarterly coal production lowest since the early 1980s.* [Online]. Eia.gov. Available at: http://www.eia.gov/todayinenergy/detail.php?id=26612. [Accessed 18 Jul. 2017].

Sanderson, H., Hancock, T. and Lewis, L. (2017). 'Electric cars: China's battle for the battery market.' *Financial Times.* [Online]. Available at: https://www.ft.com/content/8c94a2f6-fdcd-11e6-8d8e-a5e3738f9ae4?mhq5j=e3 [Accessed 18 Jul. 2017].

Sims, R. and Schaeffer, R. (2014). *Transport.* Fifth Assessment Report of the Intergovernmental Panel on Climate Change. [Online]. IPCC. pp.599-670. Available at: https://www.ipcc.ch/pdf/assessment-report/ar5/wg3/ipcc_wg3_ar5_chapter8.pdf [Accessed 18 Jul. 2017].

Tianjie, M. (2017). 'China's Ambitious New Clean Energy Targets.' *The Diplomat.* [Online] Available at: http://thediplomat.com/2017/01/chinas-ambitious-new-clean-energy-targets/ [Accessed 19 Jul. 2017].

Unfccc.int. (n.d.). *The Paris Agreement - main page.* [Online]. Available at: http://unfccc.int/paris_agreement/items/9485.php [Accessed 18 Jul. 2017].

Design Optimization for Magnesium Parts Used in Automotive Body Structure

Abed Alaswad

School of Engineering and the Built Environment, Birmingham City University, Millennium Point, Birmingham, UK. B4 7AP.

E-mail: abed.alaswad@bcu.ac.uk

Abstract

Driven by the climate change issue, and the global response to it, a significant effort has been spent, over the last few decades, on the lightweight industry as it has been proven to lead to a less fuel consumption, less pollution, along with better drivability and performance. In this regard, magnesium is considered to have an excellent potential as it is one of the lightest structural metals offering great weight saving. However, due to a number of technical and commercial obstacles, magnesium has not been promoted effectively on a wide scale. Therefore, a good deal of research is needed to overcome these barriers, aiming towards bigger involvement of magnesium in automotive and aerospace industries. In this research, the viability of using magnesium alloys in structural components in automotive industry is investigated by exploring the crashworthiness behaviour for different metals under different loading conditions. The effect of thickness increases on the absorbed energy and the material weight will be covered. A proposal on how to effectively measure crashworthiness for magnesium and how to improve its behaviour in energy absorption is described.

Keywords

Crashworthiness, Energy Absorption, Impact, Lightweight.

INTRODUCTION

Lightweight research is increasingly considered as a major trend in component design and development, especially in automotive and aerospace industries. Reducing the vehicle's mass improves the fuel economy, decreases the greenhouse gasses emission, and enhances the vehicle performance attributes such as braking and handling. One approach to gain less weight is to explore the application of proper light materials in applications where heavy metals, such as steel and cast iron, has been traditionally used. Materials used must also show specific properties depending on the component's function and position alongside a reasonable cost compared with the presently employed material. However, it has to be mentioned that, new designs and manufacturing techniques might be considered when new lighter materials used, while cost alongside other outputs like robustness and reliability must be decided by looking on the whole picture. For an example, it is well known that magnesium and aluminium alloys are more expensive than steel and cast iron. However, cast products made of aluminium and magnesium could be potentially considered cheaper than those made of cast iron and steel, based on what aluminium or magnesium can offer for these parts including better machinability, ability to have thinner and more variable wall dimensions, closer tolerances, reduced assemblies, along with less melting/ metal forming heat needed (Joost and Krajewski, 2017).

The weight breakdown of the existing vehicle is presented in (Table 1), from which it is shown that primary focus must be paid on the body chassis, and interior areas when exploring light weighting technologies.

TABLE 1: Weighting distribution among automobile engineering systems (Abbott, 2003).

System	% Weight of Total	% Weight Reduction Goal	% of Total Weight Reduction
Body in White	29.8	41.6	12.4
Exterior Systems	5.4	-4.8	-0.26
Chassis	25.2	26.2	6.5
Powertrain	19.3	0	0
Interior	12.3	18.8	2.3
Electrical	2.6	16.6	0.43
Indirect Materials	5.4	19.3	1.04

MAGNESIUM FOR BODY STRUCTURE

Magnesium (density $\approx 1.8\,g/cm^3$) is 33% lighter than aluminium and 75% lighter than steel/cast-iron components. The corrosion resistance of modern, high-purity magnesium alloys is better than that of conventional aluminium die-cast alloys (Cole, 2007), but magnesium components have also mechanical property disadvantages and require unique design for application on automotive products. Although its tensile yield strength is about the same, magnesium has lower ultimate tensile strength than aluminium (25% less), 35% lower fatigue strength, and creep strength that is 15% less than Al A380 at 20°C and 65% less at 130°C. The modulus of magnesium alloys is 40% lower than aluminium and hardness is 25% lower; thermal expansion coefficient is 15% greater. However, it is important to note that strength and modulus limitations can often be overcome by suitable ribbing and supports Cole and Sherman (1995).

The light weight properties of magnesium along beside its excellent structural integrity and high pressure die castability make magnesium alloys popular for non-structural components that are usually made by high pressure die casting such as engine components and steering wheels. However, the use of magnesium alloys in structural parts has not been equally populated. For structural parts, the crashworthiness behaviour which is the ratio of the impact energy absorbed to the part weight is of a great importance to insure safety of passengers together with light weighting. It has been found that a magnesium car body structure with equal stiffness can be 60% or 20% lighter than steel or aluminium design, respectively. Therefore, more attention must be paid to wrought magnesium alloys which generally exhibit higher strength and ductility than casted magnesium alloys.

An assessment of the energy absorption of steel and magnesium has been carried out using a vertical strut subjected to impact loading. During the strut compression, the energy absorbed by the strut corresponds to the area under the curve and is mostly dependent on the plastic behaviour before fracture. The equation developed for rigid plastic behaviour is given by Grzebieta and Murray (1985, 1986):

$$\delta^P = \frac{M_P^2}{DP^2}\left[1-\left(\frac{P}{P_y}\right)^2\right]^2$$

Equation [1]

By inputting the properties of mild steel and magnesium AM60, Figure 1 shows a comparison of steel plates 2.5 and 10 mm thick and AM60 plates 5 and 10 mm thick. A comparison of the areas under the curves of steel and magnesium shows that the energy absorbed by the 10 mm AM60 is close to an order of magnitude higher than for the same weight of steel. At half the weight of steel (5 mm AM60 compared to 2.5 mm steel) the energy absorbed by magnesium is greater. This indicates that a significant benefit can be obtained by applying magnesium to structural applications. The model's validity has been tested previously for steel and fits well (Abbott, 2003, Grzebieta and Murray, 1985).

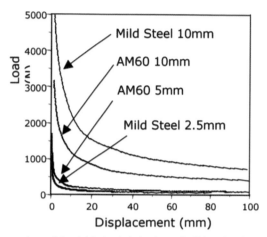

FIGURE 1: A comparison of the rigid plastic behaviour of mild steel and AM60 (Abbott, 2003).

WALL THICKNESS OPTIMIZATION OF MAGNESIUM PARTS USED IN BODY STRUCTURE

Optimization techniques are recommended to work in line with the analysis and numerical modelling to insure the light weighting besides improving crashworthiness behaviour. Design variables can be the wall thicknesses or any other dimensional parameter. Parrish *et al.* (2012) employed magnesium alloys (AZ31) counterparts in car body structure to replace 22 steel parts. A numerical model that was developed at the National Crash Analysis Centre (NCAC) and validated by NCAC for a Full Frontal Impact (FFI) scenario10, was used. Impact criteria considered were the side impact (SIDE) and Offset Frontal Impact (OFI) were simulated in LS-DYNA Finite Element (FE) code with each crash scenario following the Federal Motor Vehicle Safety Standards (FMVSS) 11 for impact velocity and impact angle. A following optimization study was carried out where the thickness of the twenty-two selected vehicle parts are used as design variables. The twenty-two selected parts account for approximately 40% of the energy absorption in each crash scenario and have a mass of approximately 105 kg compared to the vehicle mass of approximately 1300 kg.

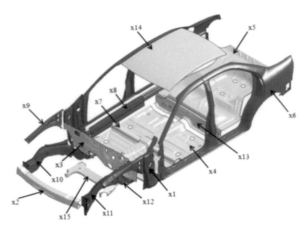

FIGURE 2: Selected vehicle components and associated part numbers (Kiani *et al.*, 2014).

In an extending work, Kiani *et al.* (2014), investigated weight reduction of a car by replacing the steel baseline by magnesium counterparts. A multidisciplinary design optimization along with finite element modelling has been applied, while the wall thicknesses of the parts were selected as design variables. Crashworthiness and vibration responses of the FE model were treated as design constraints. Substitution of magnesium alloy and design optimization resulted in an overall weight saving of 46.7 kg indicating an approximate mass reduction of 44.3% compared to the baseline steel design. Logan *et al.* (2006) show that magnesium body structure not only offers more than 40% weight reduction as compared to a conventional steel structure, but it also significantly improves the structural performance.

Energy absorption characteristics and deformation behaviour for three-point bending were investigated by Zhou *et al.* (2016) for empty and polyurethane foam-filled magnesium alloy AZ31B thin-walled beams, and compared with the characteristics and behaviour of steel DC04 beams. Both AZ31B and DC04 beams show an effect of strain rate on the energy absorption. AZ31B significantly outperforms DC04 in terms of specific energy absorption, but it fractures earlier. For applications that require limited deformation, there is a possibility to develop lightweight auto-body structures such as rocker rails by substituting foam-filled AZ31B structures for mild steel structures, while maintaining or exceeding their current crashworthiness and safety.

CONCLUSION AND FUTURE RECOMMENDATIONS

The aim of this work is to extend the optimization work which has been carried out by different researchers to decide on the optimum wall thickness which achieves the best possible light weighting of the part while maintaining the same crashworthiness and absorbed energy. In this regard, a finite element modelling will be built for the bumper part (as a start) to simulate the dynamic and quasi static situations. The model will be validated using analytical and experimental data. FE analysis will affectively allow investigating the effect of each design parameter (not only the wall thickness) on the crashworthiness behaviour of the part. The effect of each design parameter on the crashworthiness, weight, and other outputs will be studied in detail. A further multi- response optimization will be established to study, for specific cases, what are the optimal designs required to achieve the highest crashworthiness / weight proportion, and /or any other realistic outputs. The proposed analysis and optimization results will not only generate design guidelines for automotive companies that are currently using magnesium, but will open new big markets with some automotive companies that are still not convinced to work with magnesium like Volkswagen.

References

Abbott, T., Easton, M. and Schmidt, R. (2003). Magnesium for crashworthy components. Magnesium Technology, Edited by Howard I. Kaplan TMS (The Minerals, Metals & Materials Society).

Cole, G. S. (2007). Magnesium vision 2020: a north american automotive strategic vision of magnesium. USAMP report.

Cole, G. S. and Sherman A. M. (1995). Light weight materials for automotive applications. *Materials Characterization*, 35, (1) 3- 9.

Grzebieta, R. H. and Murray, N. W. (1985). The static behaviour of struts with initial kinks at their centre point. *Int. J. Impact Engineering*, 3, (3), 155-165.

Grzebieta, R. H. and Murray, N. W. (1986). Energy absorption of an initially imperfect strut subjected to an impact load. *Int. J. Impact Engineering*, 4, (3), 147-159.

Joost, W. and Krajewski P. (2017). Towards magnesium alloys for high-volume automotive applications. *Scripta Materialia*, 128, 107- 112.

Kiani, M., Gandikota, I., Rais-Rohan, M. and Motoyama, K. (2014). Design of lightweight magnesium car body structure under crash and vibration constraints. *Journal of Magnesium and Alloys*, 2, (2) 99- 108.

Logan, S., Kizyma, A., Patterson, C., Rama, S., *et al.* (2006). Lightweight magnesium intensive body structure, SAE Technical Paper 2006-01-0523.

Parrish, A., Rais-Rohani, M. and Najafi, A. (2012). *Int. J. Crashworthiness*, 17, 259-281.

Zhou, P., Beeh, E., Kriescher, M., Friedrich, H., and Kopp, G. (2016). Experimental comparison of energy absorption characteristics of polyurethane foam- filled magnesium and steel beam in bending. *International Journal of Impact Engineering*, 93, 76- 87.

Towards Improvement of Formability of Magnesium Alloys

Michal Krzyzanowski[4], Janusz Majta[*], Krzysztof Muszka[*], Marta Slezak[&] and David Randman[&]

School of Engineering and the Built Environment, Birmingham City University, Millennium Point, Curzon Street, Birmingham, B4 7AP, UK.
[*] Faculty of Metals Engineering and Industrial Computer Science, AGH University of Science and Technology, Mickiewicza 30, Krakow 30-059, Poland.
[&] Special Metals Wiggin Ltd., Holmer Road, Hereford, HR4 9SL, UK (formerly at The University of Sheffield)
Email: michal.krzyzanowski@bcu.ac.uk

Abstract
The current research activities on improvement of formability of Mg alloys leading the way toward obtaining better structural materials with both decent ductility and impressive strength are presented. The recently developed method combining accumulative angular drawing (AAD) with wire drawing is used as a testing method to effectively induce severe plastic deformation (SPD) effects into the drawn metallic material. The influence of the combined deformation effects on the accumulated deformation energy and microstructural inhomogeneity in the h.c.p. wires is discussed with respect to possibilities of formation of ultrafine-grained and multi-layered structures. The dynamic material modelling (DMM) approach is presented and demonstrated as a useful tool to predict workability of Mg alloys. The approach is based upon the fundamental principles of the continuum mechanics of large plastic flow, the physical system modelling and irreversible thermodynamics. In addition, the results of the recent rheological testing of AZ91, WE43B and E21 Mg alloys with different chemical compositions and the powder bed generation model for cases of laser-assisted additive manufacturing AM technology are discussed.

Keywords
Formability of Mg-alloys, Sever Plastic Deformation, Simulation, Dynamic Material Modelling, Rheological Testing

INTRODUCTION

It is the lowest density of any structural metals that makes magnesium and its alloys to be very attractive materials for a wide range of structural applications, especially where weight saving is of paramount significance, such as in automotive or aerospace industries. Magnesium is the lightest engineering structural metallic material, it is 35% lighter than aluminium and 78% lighter than steel (Furuya *et al.*, 2000). To attain lower weight of vehicles, different materials are also considered such as aluminium and titanium. However, magnesium is getting overwhelming interest of researchers amongst the lightweight materials (Chang *et al.*, 2004; Cavaliere and De Marco, 2006; Kaneko *et al.*, 2000; Lihui *et al.*, 2011; Zheng *et al.*, 2011; Yoshihara, *et al.*, 2003; Yuang, *et al.*, 2008). At present, the leading automotive industry manufacturers, such as General Motors, Ford and Chrysler are increasingly applying magnesium for mirror brackets, instrument panels, steering wheels and transfer cases. Apart from being the lightest structural metal, magnesium has average ductility, good recyclability, improved vibration and noise characteristics in comparison to

---

[4] Author to whom any correspondence should be addressed.

other structurally used metals. Despite the attractiveness as a lightweight structural metal, the use of traditional Mg alloys is limited mainly due to its poor formability, corrosion resistance, and a limited strength capacity at elevated temperatures. Besides all mentioned applications, the current use of magnesium is only a fraction comparing to aluminium (Lihui *et al.*, 2011). The forming of magnesium alloys is still difficult, and its plastic deformation mechanisms are not yet clarified. Magnesium has limited ductility at room temperature comparing to aluminium and steel. The reason is because the h.c.p. structure has fewer operative slip systems. Alternative slip systems, other than basal slip, have to be activated during the deformation process of Mg-alloys to extend its utility. Therefore, twinning, as another deformation mechanism, can play an important role in coordinating the plastic deformation. Experimental investigations have revealed that texture plays a significant role in improving or impairing the ductility of Mg-alloys. The activated deformation modes highly depend on the orientations of the grains, in such way depend on the texture, the deformation path and the mechanical process. The combined effect of grain boundary strengthening, second phase strengthening and activation of non-basal slip mechanisms may lead the way to better Mg-alloys, which will have both decent ductility and impressive strength. The specific structure of magnesium alloys is also responsible for the reduced melting point and make the alloys less resistant to corrosion (Kim and Lee, 2010).

In recent years, different techniques are developed aiming to overcome the above mentioned problems. Among them, an application of elevated temperatures is widely accepted in order to improve ductility of alloys having h.c.p. structure (Abu-Farhaa and Khraisheh, 2006). Initially, the technique utilising elevated temperatures for obtaining a significant ductility have been introduced on aluminium and titanium alloys. In the light metal industry, it is known as superplasticity, which is based on the ability of a metallic material to exhibit high elongations prior to failure. It has to be noted, that titanium alloys have h.c.p. structure similar to Mg-alloys. It can suggest that many findings applicable for titanium alloys can also be considered for improvement of magnesium alloys. However, to utilise the effect of superplasticity, both the grain size of the metallic material should be less than 10μm and the strain rate should be within the range of $10^{-2} - 10^{-4}$ s^{-1}, which significantly restricts their industrial applications. In addition to that, the operating temperature should be approximately equal to half of the melting temperature of the given metallic material (Abu-Farha, F. and Khraisheh, M., 2007). There have been several endeavours to overcome the mentioned technical restrictions. As a result of such efforts, the high strain rate superplasticity technique was developed allowing to obtain 280% elongation at the strain rate of 10^{-2} s^{-1} for AZ91 magnesium alloy (Mabuchi *et al.*, 1997). Other researchers achieved 283% elongation for ZK61 magnesium alloy at the same strain rate (Watanabe *et al.*, 1999). As for higher grain size, there is a work reporting achievement of 200% elongation on AZ80 alloy with the grain size of 35 μm at 350 °C (Changa *et al.*, 2003) as well as achievement of low temperature superplasticity for AZ31, AZ91 and ZK60 magnesium alloys (Bussiba *et al.*, 2001; Watanabe *et al.*, 2000; Thuramalla *et al.*, 2003).

Magnesium alloys, as a group of metallic materials, have higher specific strength than their counterparts such as steel or aluminium, in such way offer potential for reducing weight in aerospace applications. Mg has been approved by Joint Aviation standards and NASA standards that it can be used in areas that are not prone to corrosion. However, conventional processing techniques, such as different thermo-mechanical processes, are not as amendable for production of thin-gage parts and claddings proposed for space applications. Development of additive manufacturing (AM) techniques offers a novel fabrication approach, potentially easy producing cladding and thin-gage parts and also incorporating these alloys into compositionally-graded structures. AM technology is developed fast due to its ability of near-net shape fabrication of monolithic components, possibility of reducing lead-time, energy consumption and cost (Frazier, W.E., 2014). At present, only a few reports are available in the literature on AM of pure magnesium (Chi *et al.*, 2011; Hu, D., Wang *et al.*, 2015), magnesium alloys [Wei *et al.*, 2014; Wei *et al.*, 2015) or the mixture of magnesium (Zhang *et al.*, 2012) using selective laser melting (SLM). Apart from the well-known opinion that the fine powders of magnesium alloys are flammable and explosive, the most of laser energy is reflected due to the low absorption of magnesium during SLM, which results in not sufficient efficiency and increases the risk of breakdown of the laser device (Al-Kazzaz *et al.*, 2008).

The outcome of current research curried out at Birmingham City University in collaboration with AGH University of Science and Technology in Krakow (Poland) on improvement of formability of h.c.p structural materials is discussed in this work leading the way toward obtaining Mg-alloys with improved mechanical properties. The work covers application of AAD technique to induce SPD effects into the drawn metallic material, the dynamic material modelling (DMM) approach, as a useful tool to predict workability of Mg alloys, the results of the recent rheological testing of Mg alloys with different chemical compositions and also the powder bed generation model applicable for cases of laser-assisted AM technology, where knowledge of the packing structure and packing density of the powder bed is required.

ANGULAR ACCUMULATIVE DRAWING

The SPD process investigated within the work was designed to manufacture ultrafine-grained metal products via complex processing route involving the processes of accumulative angular drawing (AAD), sometimes combined with wire drawing (WD), and wire flattening (WF) (Majta *et al.*, 2016; Muszka *et al.*, 2013). The AAD process is characterised by a complex strain path history as a combined effect of wire diameter reduction, bending, tension and torsion.

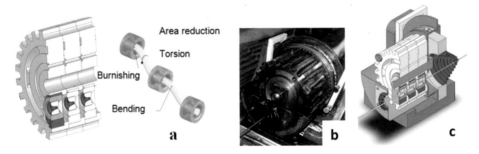

FIGURE 1: The schematic representation of the AAD process (a), the experimental rig (b) and the representation of the AAD die assembly (c).

The strain path effects the microstructural changes in the final product allowing for obtaining high level of microstructure inhomogeneity and development of dislocation structure. In the current version of the laboratory AAD rig (Figure 1), the diameter of the initial rod is 6.5 mm and the smallest diameter after AAD and WD operations is about 1.96 mm. The wires can be additionally deformed by WF with equivalent strain of 0.42 to the thickness of 400 μm. The total strain accumulated in all mentioned subsequent operations is about $\varepsilon = 2.81$. Initially, during AAD operation, the outer layers of the deformed wire undergo strain hardening, which leads to high inhomogeneity of strain in the cross section of the wire shirting the plastic deformation zone towards the centre of the wire. Different plastic strain inhomogeneity can be obtained as a result of three different combinations of the die positioning, such as linear, alternate, and stepped (Figure 2a, b and c). Significantly higher values of accumulation of deformation energy are achieved in AAD comparing to the conventional wire drawing which leads to significant refining and potential deformation induced softening of the microstructure, *i.e.* development of dislocation substructure (Figure 2d).

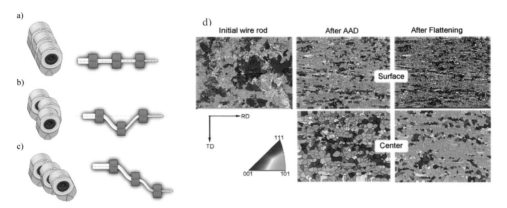

FIGURE 2: Different positioning of the drawing dies in the AAD (a, b, c) and microstructure evolution at the different stages of the combined deformation process (d).

The process reduces intensity of the tensile stress component in the central zone of the deformed wire. It has been shown that the uniform elongation and elongation to fracture were clearly higher for ADD processed wires. The processed wires show very attractive combination of mechanical properties due to formation of refined microstructure in the outer layers. The high deformation inhomogeneity and resulted refined microstructure influence significant increase in ductility that can potentially improve applicability of the metallic alloys with h.c.p. structure. The complex deformation mechanisms induced by continuous strain path changes influence elongation of grains and formation of wavy lamellar structure. The high accumulation of deformation energy leads to defragmentation of those lamella into dislocation cells. There is a possibility to determine the point where necking occurs analysing the true stress-strain curves obtained directly from tensile testing of the obtained wires. The point of necking corresponds to the point of tensile instability. Uniform plastic deformation occurs as long as the true stress is below the value of work hardening rate, $d\sigma/d\varepsilon < \sigma$. The uniform deformation stops and necking begins when the two quantities are equal. This method is known as Considère (necking) criterion (Considère, 1892).

DYNAMIC MATERIAL MODELLING APPROACH

The application of Mg alloys requires reliable simulation tools for predicting the forming capabilities, the structural response to mechanical loads and the lifetime of the component. The results of the plane strain compression testing of Mg Alloy Elektron™ 675 performed at various temperatures within the range of 400 - 500°C and 1.0, 5.0 and 10s^{-1} strain rates are used in this part of the work (Randman, 2010). The specimens were deformed to the strain of 0.6. Based on the obtained flow curves, processing maps are performed applying Dynamic Material Modelling (DMM) approach (Prasad and Sasidhara, 2003) . The approach is based on the fundamental principles of the continuum mechanics of large plastic flow, the physical system modelling and irreversible thermodynamics. It is assumed that the workpiece is considered as a power dissipator, which can be represented as a sum of dissipator content G (power dissipated by plastic work, which is converted into heat), and dissipator co-content J (related to dynamic microstructural processes that proceed along with power dissipation and responsible for the intrinsic workability of the material - *e.g.* dynamic recovery, dynamic recrystallization, dissolution of growth of particles, strain-induced phase transformation, *etc.*). The latter term, J co-content, is evaluated as a function of the temperature and the strain rate at the constant strain. In the DMM approach, a power dissipation efficiency between heat and microstructural changes is a measure of material's workability (Figure 3a).

Based on the above-mentioned experimental data, the processing map (P-map) is constructed being an explicit representation of the response of a material to the imposed process parameters in terms of the microstructural mechanisms. P-map is prepared by combination of the power dissipation map, illustrated by isoclines, with the instability map, plotted in the frame of temperature and the log strain rate at a constant strain. The variations of the instability parameter, as a function of the strain rate and the temperature, allows for plotting the instability maps (Figure 3b). The regions on the map, where instability parameter is lower than zero, correspond to the microstructural instabilities (the unstable flow) in the material. This parameter is considered to be an important warning when designing the technology of plastic deformation for a specific material. Another useful tool to predict material behaviour is numerical simulation. Commercially available Finite Element Modelling (FEM) packages can be easily used to perform numerical simulations at a wide range of the process parameters. Figure 4 illustrates an example of the plastic strain distribution in Mg Alloy Elektron™ 675 specimen that was deformed in the safe zone under 0.6 strain, the temperature of 420 °C and the strain rate of $1s^{-1}$.

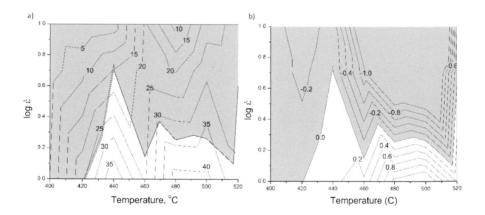

FIGURE 3: The example of the processing map based upon Prasad criterion (a) and the contour map for instability parameter ξ_1 (b) – true strain 0.6.

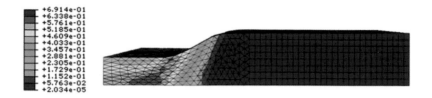

FIGURE 4: The logarithmic strain distribution in the specimen deformed at 420°C with the strain rate of 1s⁻¹ as an example of the numerical simulation within "the safe zone".

REOLOGICAL TESTING OF MG ALLOYS

Utilization of Mg alloys depends mainly on casting technology. For instance, more favourable workable characteristics can be achieved in thixoforming. The study of the properties of existing Mg alloys and the search of the new Mg and Al based metallic compositions that can be deformed and formed in the semi-solid state is the aim of this part of the research activities. High-temperature rheological research is modern research, allowing for obtaining the key information on the influence of forces and the time of their impact on a specific material. Such information is essential for designing of the forming processes in semi-solid states. The work focuses on rheological characterisation of the light metallic alloys in liquid and semi-solid states, on development of rheological models allowing for calculation of the rheological parameters taking into account different chemical compositions and on combination of the rheological and microstructure analysis in order to improve the thixoforming processing. Such comprehensive and accurate description of the rheological behaviour seems to be a key factor for development and optimisation of semi-solid forming of Mg alloys. Rheological testing of Mg alloys is challenging due to the high reactivity of the materials. Viscosity is the main rheological parameter considered in the thixoforming processes, in other words, semi-solid metal forming (SSM) processes. It is an indicator defining the capability of the metallic material to fill a mould and it is the parameter that determines the force required to deform the material. The rheological tests are carried out using a high-temperature rheometer. The FRS1600 rheometer is a high precision instrument, as illustrated in Figure 5. It is one of the few instruments of this type that enables measurements at high temperatures acceptable for testing a broad range of liquids. It can carry out the relevant measurements for both high and low viscosity liquids due to the broad measurement range of torque, from 0.05 mNm to 200 mNm. The Searle type cup and bob system is used for the measurements. The bobs of 16 mm diameter with perforated surfaces and the cups of 30 mm diameter with smooth inner surfaces are used for the testing. The tools are made of low-carbon steel.

The results of testing of AZ91, WE43B and E21 Mg alloys with different chemical compositions are presented in the form of flow curves (Figure 6). The preliminary results indicated that the highest shear stresses, around of 50 Pa, were obtained for AZ91 alloy, while only the stresses within the range of 10 – 20 Pa have been registered for E21 and WE43B alloys. Both E21 and WE43B alloys contain rare earth elements, such as yttrium, neodymium, gadolinium, which may influence the changes in the shear stress. Further rheological testing of the materials with various contents of the rare earth metals are planned to verify the above-mentioned statement. In addition, a tendency towards non-linear growth of the shear stress with the growth of the strain rate is noticed that may indicate decline in the dynamic viscosity coefficient as a result of the applied load.

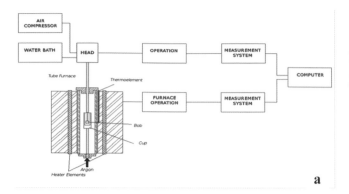

a

b

FIGURE 5: The schematic representation (a) and the photograph (b) of FRS1600 high temperature rheometer used for testing of Mg alloys

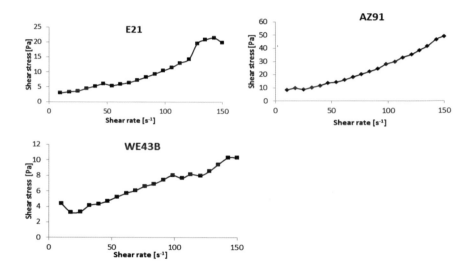

FIGURE 6: Flow curves obtained for the different Mg alloys: E21, AZ91 and WE43B.

LASER ASSISTED ADDITIVE MANUFACTURING

As it has been already mentioned, the most of laser energy is reflected due to the low absorption of magnesium during SLM. The absorption of laser radiation by compact material is influenced by the laser wave length, the nature of the material, the surface condition and the temperature. Topological boundary conditions, additionally to the mentioned above, become additional influencing factors in the absorption of powder bulks. The absorption of metal powders is different from the absorption of compact metals. At room temperatures, the absorption coefficient of metal alloy powders is within the range of 30 - 45% for CO_2-radiation and for an average particle size of about 30μm. The same coefficient is between 2% and 8% for compact, clean and polished metals and for the same wave length of laser radiation. The enhanced absorption of powders can be explained by the special topology of powder beds and by the oxide scale formed on the particle surfaces. The latter can be responsible for up to 80% of the absorptivity (Wagner, 2003). In laser sintering, the absorption decreases during heating until the absorption of the melt, which is about 11-13% for steel melts. The Cellular Automata (CA) based model of powder bed generation has been developed recently as a useful numerical tool for generation of the desirable packing characteristics, such as various particle size distributions and packing densities, depending on different deposition parameters (Krzyzanowski et al., 2016). The characteristics of the powder bed are very important for its subsequent laser assisted densification by sintering or melting, which is a crucial step in SLM of Mg alloys. The usefulness of the model is obvious for cases of laser-assisted integrated ALM models based on finite element (FM) methodology, where knowledge of the packing structure and packing density of the powder bed is required. The model considers an introduction of the particles either from a specified point or randomly across a specified area and can include cases with no, partial or multiple restructuring and calculates the movement of the particles until they reach the local minimum in contact with other particles of the deposit or the basement.

CONCLUSION

One of the major barriers to greatly increased Mg alloys use is still their poor formability. The brief review of the state-of-the-art findings, methodologies and current research activities into solving different problems related to formability of Mg alloys has been presented. Magnesium alloys are expected to play an important role in materials of the next generation, lightening the total product weight replacing aluminium and steel parts. Demands have been risen in automotive, electronics and aerospace industries to reduce the total product weight. Magnesium alloys have the highest strength-to-weight ratio of all the structural metals. They also received global attention from the environmental preservation point of view.

Acknowledgements
This work was supported partly by the EPSRC (UK) under grant EP/L505158/1, NSC (Poland) under grants DEC-2013/09/B/ST8/00141, DEC-2012/05/B/ST8/00215 and DEC-2015/19/B/ST8/01064 and also by NCRD (Poland) under grant 007/151/L-5/13/NCBR/2014.

References
Abu-Farhaa, F. and Khraisheh, M. (2006). On the superplastic forming of the AZ31 magnesium alloy. Proceedings of the 7th International Conference on Magnesium, Dresden.
Abu-Farha, F. and Khraisheh, M., (2007). Analysis of superplastic deformation of AZ31 magnesium alloy, *Advanced Engineering Materials*, 9, [9], 777-783.
Al-Kazzaz, H., Medraj, M., Cao, X. and Jahazi, M. (2008). Nd:Yag laser welding of aerospace grade ZE41A magnesium alloy: modeling and experimental investigations. *Mater. Chem. Phys.*, 109, 61–76.
Bussiba, A., Artzy, A. B., Shtechman, A., Iftergan, S. and Kupiec, M. (2001). Grain refinement of AZ31 and AZ60 Mg alloys towards superplasticity studies. *Materials Science and Engineering A*, 302, 56-62.
Cavaliere, P. and De Marco, P. P. (2006). Effect of friction stir processing on mechanical and microstructural properties of AM60B magnesium alloy. *Journal of Materials Science*, 41, [11], 3459-3464.
Chang, C., Lee, C. and Huang, J. (2004). Cavitation characteristics in AZ31 Mg alloys during LTSP or HSRSP. *Acta Materialia*, 52, 3111-3122.
Changa, T. C., Wang, J. Y., Ob, C. M. and Lee, S. (2003). Grain refining of magnesium alloy AZ31 by rolling, *Journal of Materials Processing Technology*, 140, [1-3], 588-593.
Chi, C. N., Savalani, M. and Man, H. C. (2011). Fabrication of magnesium using selective laser melting technique. *Rapid Prototyp. J.*, 17, 479–490.
Considère, A., (1892). Utilité des chemins de fer d'intérêt local, *Annales des ponts et chaussées*, 7ème série, T. III, chap. IV, 298-312.
Frazier, W. E. (2014). Metal additive manufacturing: A review. *J. Mater. Eng. Perform.*, 23, 1917–1928.
Furuya, H., Kogiso N., Matunaga, S. and Senda, K. (2000). Applications of magnesium alloys for aerospace structure systems. *Materials Science Forum*, 350-352, 341-148.

Hu, D., Wang, Y., Zhang, D., Hao, L., Jiang, J., Li, Z. and Chen, Y. (2015). Experimental investigation on selective laser melting of bulk net-shape pure magnesium. *Mater. Manuf. Process.*, 30, 1298–1304.

Kaneko, J., Sugamata, M., Numa, M., Nishikawa, Y. and Takada, H. (2000). Effect of texture on the mechanical properties and formability of magnesium wrought materials. *Journal of the Japan Institute of Metals*, 64, [2], 141-147.

Kim, W.J. and Lee, W.G. (2010). Enhanced Superplasticity of 1 wt.%Ca-AZ80 Mg alloy with ultrafine grains, *Advanced Materials Letters*, 64, [16], 1759-1762.

Krzyzanowski, M., Svyetlichnyy, D., Stevenson, G. and Rainforth, W. M. (2016). Powder bed generation in integrated modelling of additive layer manufacturing of orthopaedic implants, *Int. J. Adv. Manuf. Technol.*, 87, [1-4], 519-530.

Lihui, W., Tang, D., Jiang, T. D. and Yu, C. (2011). Prospect of magnesium alloy in metallurgical industry. *Journal of Wuhan Engineering Institute*, [1], 8-10.

Mabuchi, M., Iwasaki, H., Yanase, K. and Higashi, K. (1997). Low temperature superplasticity in an AZ91 magnesium alloy. *Scripta Materialia*, 36, [6], 681-686.

Majta, J., Perzynski, K., Muszka, K., Graca, P. and Madej, L. (2016). Modelling of grain refinement and mechanical response of microalloyed steel wires severely deformed by combined forming process, *Int. J. Adv. Manuf. Technol.*, DOI 10.1007/s00170-016-9203-2.

Muszka, K., Madej, L. and Majta, J. (2013). The effects of deformation and microstructure inhomogeneities in the accumulative angular drawing (AAD). *Mater. Sci. Eng. A.*, 574, 68-74.

Prasad, Y. V. R. K., Sasidhara, S. (ed.) (2003). Hot working guide: a compendium of processing maps, ASM International, Materials Park, OH.

Randman, D. (2010). Deformation mechanisms in magnesium alloy Elektron™ 675, PhD Thesis, The University of Sheffield.

Thuramalla, N. V. and Khraisheh, M. K. (2003). Effects of microstructural evolution on the stability of superplastic deformation. *Proceedings of the 2nd MIT Conference on "Computational Fluid and Solid Mechanics"*, 683-686.

Wagner, C., (2003). Untersuchungen zum Selektiven Lasersintern von Metallen, Dissertation RWTH Aachen/Germany.

Watanabe, H., Mukai, T., Ishikawa, K., Okanda, Y. and Higashi, K. (1999). Superplastic characteristics in an extruded AZ31 magnesium alloy. *Journal of Japan Institute of Light Metals*, 49, [8], 401-404.

Watanabe, H., Tsutsui, H., Mukai, T., Ishikawa, K., Okanda, Y., Kohzu, M., and Higashi, K. (2000). Superplastic behavior in commercial wrought magnesium alloys, *Materials Science Forum.*, 350-351, 171-176.

Wei, K., Gao, M., Wang, Z. and Zeng, X. (2014). Effect of energy input on formability, microstructure and mechanical properties of selective laser melted AZ91 magnesium alloy. *Mater. Sci. Eng. A*, 611, 212–222.

Wei, K., Wang, Z. and Zeng, X. (2015). Influence of element vaporization on formability, composition, microstructure, and mechanical performance of the selective laser melted mg–zn–zr components. *Mater. Lett.*, 156, 187–190.

Yoshihara, S., Nishimura, H., Yamamoto, H. and Manabe, K. (2003). Formability enhancement in magnesium alloy stamping using a local heating and cooling technique, circular cup deep drawing process. *Journal of Materials Processing Technology*, 142, [3], 609-613.

Yuang, L. F., Mori, K. I. and Tsuji, H. (2008). Deformation behaviours of magnesium alloy AZ31 in cold deep drawing, *Transactions of Nonferrous Metals Society of China*, 18, [1], 86-91.

Zhang, B., Liao, H. and Coddet, C. (2012). Effects of processing parameters on properties of selective laser melting Mg–9%Al powder mixture. *Mater. Des.*, 34, 753–758.

Zheng Quan, G., Wan Ku, T., Song, W. J. and Kang, B. S. (2011). The workability evaluation of wrought AZ80 magnesium alloy in hot compression. *Materials and Design*, 32, 4, 2462-2468.

Magnesium Alloy Die Casting Process Improvement Using the Single Minute Exchange of Dies (SMED) Method and Other Techniques.

Alan Pendry

School of Engineering and the Built Environment, Birmingham City University, Millennium Point, Birmingham, UK. B4 7AP.

Email: Alan.Pendry@bcu.ac.uk

Abstract

In the die casting process, the optimisation of machine capacity utilisation is a key goal in achieving economic throughput. The tooling changeover procedure is widely recognised as a possible area for reducing plant downtime. Following a visit to a sister plant in Canada, the SMED method has been augmented by rationalisation of procedures. Identification of internal and external activities and moving activities off-line wherever appropriate was investigated, along with the elimination of Non-Value-Added Activities wherever possible. There was also a bottleneck in the use of a single crane which may have been otherwise engaged when dies need to be changed. Other operating parameters will need to be investigated, including robotic loading and unloading. There are a number of challenges and opportunities for further downtime reduction, and this study is therefore on-going. The business case needs to be addressed and costs/benefits analysed. To this end, usage and order levels both before and after the Project will need to be monitored, and any new uptake identified. Changeover times at the UK plant have so far been reduced from 24 hours to an average of 6½ hours.

Keywords

SMED, Single Minute Exchange of Dies, Lean Manufacture, Downtime Reduction.

INTRODUCTION

Meridian Lightweight Technologies UK (Meridian) is part of a larger group, Wanfeng Auto. The UK plant is in Sutton-in-Ashfield, Nottinghamshire, with a Global Technology Centre and two production plants in Strathroy, Ontario, Canada. Changeovers at Sutton-in-Ashfield were taking 24 hours to complete, while downtime for similar operations in Strathroy is 4 hours. Following visits to the Strathroy facilities by Meridian staff, the Sutton-in-Ashfield time has so far been reduced to an average of 6½ hours. This paper considers work already undertaken in the reduction of changeover times following Single Minute Exchange of Dies (SMED) principles and introducing new methods of working. Further changes and improvements are then considered.

ASSESSMENT AND IMPROVEMENT OF CHANGEOVER PRACTICES

As recommended by Shingo in 1985 and subsequently by many others, including McIntosh *et al.* (2007) and Bicheno and Holweg (2016), the improvement process began with the documentation of the current state of the changeover process. This included Production Orders, Standard Operating Instructions and External Activities. In terms of tooling and equipment, dies, jigs and fixtures (including bolts, clamps, washers, *etc.*), tools (spanners, screwdrivers, Allen keys, *etc.*), moving/handling equipment, measurement and inspection tools and inspection instructions were considered. Changeover team members were identified, along with backup teams, and expectations documented during training.

Significant benefits were realised by involving the plant users to help with the project, particularly in the development of standardised procedures. This helped build new competencies and skills and gave ownership of (and hence promote compliance with) the process to the shop floor staff.

FIGURE 1: Throat, Sleeve, Pallet and Shot End components.

The changeover time reduction at Sutton-in-Ashfield has been achieved in a number of ways. The Strathroy changeovers were observed and video recorded and good practice following typical SMED philosophies has been adopted. The greatest savings have been made by placing Shot End components on stillages, Figure 1: these include the Sleeve (900kg), the Shot Tool (500kg) and the Throat Plate (500kg); and, together form what is basically a large syringe which forces molten magnesium alloy into the mould cavity. The throat determines the height of the shot end in relation to the specific die. These components were formerly stored separately and are still stored in another part of the facility, though palletisation means they are more readily available to the changeover team.

A crane, Figure 2, has been designated as being solely to be used for die changing during the specified changeover time. Ejector Dies (28 tonnes), Cover Dies (19 to 22 tonnes) and Trim Tools (9 tonnes) can now be loaded and unloaded sequentially. This was formerly a bottleneck in the system since the crane could have been in use elsewhere when it was needed for a changeover. The crane is now reserved purely for changeovers at the designated time and all staff have been trained in its use, with more staff also being trained to operate forklift trucks. This ensures the availability of the crane and other moving equipment when it is needed.

FIGURE 2: The Crane.

The Trim Tool was originally put in first, but his delayed die heating: dies need to be put in place first so that they can be warmed-up while the Trim Tool is being changed. Dies at ambient temperature take around 8 hours to heat up, and are in fact heated up for a minimum of 24 hours before changeover: 48 hours in some cases. Overheating a die, or heating it too quickly, leads to expansion which means dies cannot be closed. It can also weaken the tool steel. Automated cooling is used to avoid these problems.

Significant reductions in downtime have also been achieved by standardising all clamping and linking all tooling clamps to a single activating button, replacing 8 separate actuators, saving in itself around 30 minutes. Clamping Locators (Stakes) and hoses have been standardised – inlet hoses are now all 27mm and outlets 32mm, Figure 3, introducing an element of *Poke Yoke*. Quick-release couplings are now used to locate water and die-heating oil, though some dies are electronically heated.

A dedicated changeover team has been formed comprising two people with a second team available to cover absence or other unavailability of staff. A training package has been developed for the team who prepare and execute changeovers and oversee production for the first hour thereafter. This has led to standardisation and, with new procedures and methodology, consistency and a smooth operation.

Changeovers at Sutton-in-Ashfield are now scheduled at weekends when production is suspended. Die changes are started at 02:00 hours, so that by 07:00 hours on Mondays there is a full complement of staff on site with the knowledge to address any problems which may arise prior to recommencement of production.

FIGURE 3: Quick release couplings.

Everything required for a tooling changeover is delivered to the production cell 2 hours prior to the scheduled changeover. This means that kits can be checked for completeness and there is no need to wait for components or special tools. Each station also has a dedicated set of tools to facilitate the changeover, with the key to the toolbox being held by the Team Leaders to ensure completeness and availability. Activities which have been made external to the die change process include programming and process setting of die lubrication and part extraction robots.

CONCLUSIONS

Reducing the regularity of die changes by moving them to the weekend does produce other challenges. As well as paying staff to work at weekends (though this is presently justified because the hourly cost of downtime is significantly greater than the extra wages bill), for production to be maintained throughout the week, parts are built to stock. Whilst this means that money and space is being tied up, it does help the company in a number of ways: fewer changeovers means less downtime and performing them at weekends means there is less immediate pressure on production. Producing parts to be held as stock, or "building to bank" can lead to a number of disadvantages (Moinuddin, 2010) which are yet to be investigated, but in this instance does mean that agreements with customers to hold a minimum of 4 days' stock are easily met (in reality, the company likes to keep up to 7 days' worth of parts). These times were arrived at by studying the hypothetical worst-case production failure scenario.

The company is seeking to attract customers from smaller volume OEMs, particularly but not exclusively from the automotive sector. When tooling changeover times are high, it is obviously important to further reduce downtime. The reduction from 24 to 6 ½ hours has taken 18 months to achieve, and constraints at the Sutton-in-Ashfield site mean that further reductions will demand careful consideration. The 4-hour changeover at Strathroy has been helped by the fact that the plant was purpose-built, while the Sutton-in-Ashfield facility is essentially a converted warehouse space. This means that some of the practices employed at

Strathroy cannot be implemented at Sutton-in-Ashfield without considerable expense and disruption, if at all.

According to James-Moore and Gibbons (1997), McIntosh *et al.* (2007), and Bicheno and Holweg (2016), the application of Lean philosophies and techniques cannot be undertaken in isolation. Lean thinking is holistic and needs to be implemented on an organization-wide level. The next phase of this project will be to further investigate opportunities for downtime reduction. This may include an examination of upstream and downstream activities as well as business processes supporting production.

Acknowledgements
The author would like to thank Meridian Lightweight Technologies UK for financial support and permission to present this paper. The views expressed in this paper are those of the author and do not necessarily represent those of the Meridian Lightweight Technologies UK. Special thanks to Mr. M. Colbert in assisting with the research programme.

References
Bicheno, J. and Holweg, M. (2016). The Lean Toolbox (5th Ed). Picsie. ISBN-13: 978-0956830753.

James-Moore, S. M. and Gibbons, A. (1997). *International Journal of Operations & Production Management*, 17, [9], 911-899.

McIntosh, R., Owen, G. Culley, S. and Mileham, T. (2007). Changeover improvement: reinterpreting Shingo's "SMED" methodology. In *IEEE Transactions on Engineering Management*, 54, [1], 98-111. doi: 10.1109/TEM.2006.889070.

Moinuddin, K. (2010). Single Minute Exchange of Dies (SMED). http://www.processexcellencenetwork.com/business-process-management-bpm/articles/single-minute-exchange-of-dies-smed

Shingo, S. (1985). A revolution in manufacturing: the SMED system. Productivity Press. ISBN 0915299038.

Downtime Solutions to High Pressure Die Casts (HPDC) Exchange in Meridian Lightweight Technologies

Fawaz Y Annaz, Ian Hawkins[*] and Steve Howard[*]

School of Engineering and the Built Environment, Birmingham City University, Millennium Point, Birmingham, B4 7AP, UK.
Email: fawaz.annaz@bcu.ac.uk

[*]Meridian Lightweight Technologies, Orchard Way, Calladine Park, Sutton-In-Ashfield, Nottinghamshire, NG171JU.
Emails: ihawkins@meridian-mag.com ; showard@meridian-mag.com

Abstract

High pressure die casting (HPDC) is the process of injecting (under high pressure) molten metal into a steel die. It is one of the fastest and most economical manufacturing techniques for mass-producing high-quality metal components. Dies are reusable and are machined to the exact design of the component to be cast, into which molten metals are either poured or injected. Die casting has the advantages of producing uniform components with good surface finish, accurate dimensions, and little post-machining. The process is suitable for producing high volumes of complex-shaped thin-walled parts, with high degree of repeatability and accuracy. Magnesium alloys enjoy unique solidification characteristics over other metals, and are said to have better castability. Unlike molten aluminium, magnesium does not attack iron, therefore, it can be melted and held in steel crucibles. Magnesium alloy casting dates back to 1921 when Dow Chemical began producing magnesium pistons, and by the World War II their casting technology was well developed. In 1981, Meridian Lightweight Technologies, began magnesium die-casting, and to date remains the world's largest components producer, catering for the automotive industry. The company caters for international clients in the automotive industry. The process utilises heavy die casting machines (DCMs) with other secondary machining. Often it is necessary to replace or exchange these heavy die casts, so as to cater for different products. It is the time taken to shift or switch these dies that increases the downtime. The problem is further magnified when client companies place small orders, which makes the overall process economically unviable. It is the aim of this research is to improve downtime by proposing innovative alternatives to DCMs, deploying mechanisms, and the inclusion of redundancy to frequently failing components.

Keywords

Downtime, Robotics, Die-Casting

INTRODUCTION

Background

Magnesium was first discovered by Sir Humphrey Davy in 1808, where he developed methods to isolate the element (Brown, 2009). Sir Humphrey is also known for recognising the appealing properties of laughing gas over alcohol, and often inhaled it before giving public lectures. Other inventions by Sir Humphry include the safety lamp for miners, however, many argue that his most important discovery was that of Michael Faraday, who was successful in extracting magnesium using electrolysis in 1833. However, its commercial production by electrolysis is credited to Robert Bunsen in 1952 (Bodanis, 2011).

Structural applications of magnesium were mostly limited to Germany before finding its way to the United States. Shortly after World War I, Dow Chemicals developed the alloy 'Dowmetal' (a refined magnesium alloy, with 6% Aluminium and 0.5% percent Manganese).

Dowmetal proved extremely profitable for Dow Chemical as the alloy of choice for the automotive and aviation industries. The company's fortunes were further boosted by John Joseph Grebe (a significant member in the company), who perfected a method of extracting magnesium from sea water. Thus, seawater became the main source, as a cubic mile of seawater contains six million tons of magnesium metal (Carpenter, 2017).

Application to Automotive
The unique properties of magnesium made it very attractive to the automotive industry. Luo (2013) gave a comprehensive list of magnesium use in the automotive industry. Its first automotive application was the racing engine pistons for the Indy-500 in 1921 (Brown, 2008). Magnesium pistons were first used in Germany in 1925, and by 1937 there were over four million of them in operation. Another early application was the sandcast crankcase on the 1931 Chevrolair by GM (Powell, Krajewski, & Luo, 2010). In the United Kingdom, its commercial applications in the 1930s included the lower crankcases for city buses and transmission housings for tractors (Emley, 1966).

The Highs and Lows
HPDC was used in Germany to produce crankcases and housings (Friedrich & Mordike, 2006). The use of magnesium grew during World War II, and with the introduction of the Volkswagen Beetle its application (in the air-cooled engine and gearbox castings) was accelerated and peaked in 1971 (Friedrich & Schumann, 2001). However, the use of magnesium in structural powertrain material declined by the late 1970's, due to the greater demand of more powerful engines. Such engines operating at higher temperature necessitated the introduction of water-cooled engines as an alternative to the air-cooled engine. Furthermore, magnesium's poor corrosion resistance, saw the development of more corrosion-resistant alloys, affecting the economic viability of magnesium alloys and limiting its use to fewer applications. However, magnesium is making a comeback in vehicle light-weighting, which improves fuel economy in vehicles with internal combustion engines or other alternative energy powertrains. This has revived interest in research and development of magnesium alloy within the automotive industry in many countries around the world. Some of the current major applications include interior applications (replacing steel stampings), powertrain components and limited use in body and chassis components (Luo, 2013).

DIE CASTING TECHNOLOGY

Various magnesium die casting technologies (such as gravity sand, permanent mould, high-pressure) for aerospace, defence and automotive applications were long developed during and after World War II. This rapid growth was due to the economic advantages this technology offered in mass-production. Over the past 20 years, developments have been more focused into thin-wall die casting applications. The process itself dictates creating specific reusable moulds (or dies) that are machined to the exact design and dimensions of the cast components. Usually, melted magnesium alloys are either poured in or injected under high pressure into the die. The main appeal to the process is that it results in uniform castings with good surface finish and accurate dimensions, with little-to-no post-machining.

MERIDIAN'S JOURNEY

Meridian started magnesium die-casting back in 1981, and remains the world's largest components producers, with around 1600 employees. The company globally supplies clients from the automotive industry, utilising heavy die casting tools and other secondary machining techniques, coating, and assembly capabilities. The global presence of Meridian is reflected by the four North American, one European, and one Asian manufacturing sites, as well as three international sales offices (Meridian, 2017).

Depending on the required specifications, automobile parts are made from either AZ91D, AM60B or AM50A to achieve the uniquely set properties and performance characteristics that are best suited to specific applications. For example, powertrains and components that require durability will be made using AZ91D; safety components such as instrument panel structures and seat frames are usually made using AM60B; and, components that require further ductility with reduced strength and castability are made of AM50A. However, typically, the most commonly used specification in HPDC automotive supply industry is the AM60B, for its excellent ductility, energy absorbing properties, strength and castability.

Meridian accommodates the various order demands by replacing or exchanging the die tools. To accommodate the different placed orders, Meridian has to replace or exchange the die tools. However, due to the extremely heavy nature of these tools, it takes trained teams a period of, typically, 18-36 hours to replace a single die. This additional downtime becomes more pronounced when placed orders are small, which renders the overall process economically ineffective.

THE DIECASTING AUTOMATED CYCLES

Die Casting Machines (DCMs) are made of two halves, a fixed (stationary) die, and a movable die. A typical die casting process cycle is made of two separate-handshaking automated sub-cycles, namely the 'Part-Die-Casting Cycle' and the 'Part-Press-Trimming Cycle' (shown in Figures 1 and 2, respectively).

The Part-Die-Casting Cycle
In this cycle, the actual part is made, as briefly described in the following 5 states (shown in Figure 1):

State 1. Once a part is cast, the movable-die separates; an extract-robot moves in to extract the part from the mould (initiating the trimming process, which will be described in the next section).

State 2. A spray-robot moves in to spray the mould two halves, preparing them for the injection-process.

State 3. The DCM door closes and the spray-robot withdraws

State 4. Then, the movable-die engages with the fixed die, creating the part cavity, where the melted magnesium will be injected. The molten magnesium is then injected via an injection-piston

State 5. Once the injection is completed, the movable-die disengages, the DCM's door opens, and the extract-robot prepares to move in to extract the part from the fixed die.

States 1-5 repeat and the process is synchronized with the Part-Press-Trimming process, which starts by the positioning of the extract-robot.

The Part-Press-Trimming Cycle

This process (shown in Figure 2) involves the shearing of excess magnesium from die cast parts, which is usually melted magnesium that seeped out between the two die halves during the injection-process. Once the part is cast, the extract-robot removes to initiate the cycle, as described in the following 8 states:

State 1. Extract-robot moves in position and removes the cast part from DCM.

State 2. The DCM door closes, to initiate the next Part-Die-Casting Cycle (discussed above).

State 3. Part-quenching is initiated as the extract-robot dips the part in a cooling pool.

State 4. The robot then mounts the quenched part onto a press-trim machine, and withdraws.

State 5. The hydraulically operated jaws of the press-trim machine close, and in the process, sheers off the excess magnesium.

State 6. The jaws of the press-trim machine open, and a conveyor belt then moves in, and the cast part is dropped onto the conveyor.

State 7. The trim-press is then emptied by discarding the magnesium trimmings

State 8. The cycle is completed, with the extract-robot that was on standby closes to the DCM to repeat the cycle.

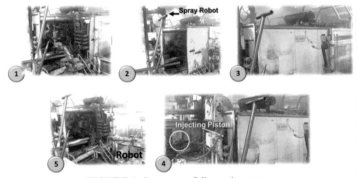

FIGURE 1: Summary of die casting stages.

FIGURE 2: Summary of trim-pressing stages.

TYPICAL DOWNTIMES

The total downtime is defined as that contributed by the Part-Die-Casting and Part-Press-Trimming Cycles, due to component and software failures or stoppage in either process. Figure 3a shows the weekly and annually logged downtimes of two DCMs (DCM5 and DCM6). Figure 3b illustrates the downtimes of parts associated with DCM5 and their percentage contributions.

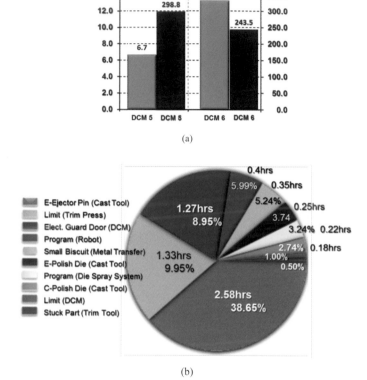

(a)

(b)

FIGURE 3: Summary of trim-pressing stages: (a) Weekly and hourly total downtime; and (b) Downtime contributions by various parts.

PROPOSED SOLUTIONS

Currently, Meridian is forced to reject orders placed by some car manufacturers, simply because these companies require small volume production, purely due to the downtime involved in replacing DCMs, thus forcing the company to decline orders that are potentially millions of pounds. The ultimate goal of this research is to conduct a feasibility study to approaches that could significantly reduce DCMs deployment. We propose three innovative alternatives that include the deployment of new mechanisms to the current DCMs, and two proposals for the development of new DCMs, as explained below:

- New Deployment Mechanism: The idea is to devise a new method, which could include the deployment of high output power hydraulics robot to shift existing

DCMs. One view is to develop a two-level architecture, with the lower level housing the hydraulic robot, which will autonomously manipulate DCMs on the upper floor. At this stage, it is difficult to draw a complete picture, therefore, placement does not necessarily involve lifting.

- Multi-Layer (Sliced-Type) Die: The movable and statics halves are proposed to be replaced by several layers that can easily be assembled by relatively moderate size robot, as shown in Figure 4. The Static (universal) Layer has pores for heating and cooling control. The pores are rerouted by an intermediate adaptive layer to heat/cool the inner cavity, where the melted metal will be injected to make the part. Therefore, the two shells and the adaptive layer are part-specific, and they are proposed to be deployed depending on the part to be made.

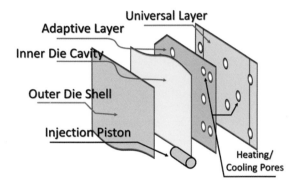

FIGURE 4: Multi-Layer (Sliced-Type) Die.

- A Wedge type Die Retainer: This design is based around a DCM with male and female diecast parts (Figure 5). The face of the die will host the female part of the system and the die has the male part. The die is lowered into the female part, and it will be in its final position when it reaches the bottom. This can be easily locked by using a ram and wedge at the top so it cannot raise up during operations. Moreover, to assist in the die change 1 or 2 rams can be fitted to the bottom of the DCM to assist in lifting the die half up. Depending on the design/angle of the wedge only minimal upward movement is needed to allow for the die half to be lifted out thus reducing the amount of time it takes for freeing up / removing the die's.

- Redundancy: This last approach is suitable to reduce downtime on the DCM. The approach is based on prior research that addressed redundancy on the all-electric aircraft (Annaz, 2014). Twenty years on the concept found its way into the development of new breed online repair robots that implements novel breed of drives (Annaz, 2016). The technology may be adapted here and target parts on the DCM that are likely to fail. For example, the mechanisms on the E-ejector pin (Cast Tool), the limit (Trim Press), the electric guard door (DCM), the robot program, and others might benefit from this technology, as they collectively contribute around 65% of the downtime (according to weekly study in Figure 3b).

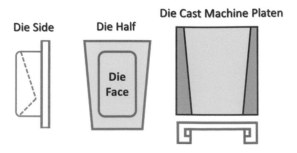

FIGURE 5: Wedge type die retainer.

CONCLUSIONS

This chapter provided an introduction to the rise, decline and resurgence of magnesium application in the automotive industry. Furthermore, a modest review of die casting was given with a brief outline of the automated cycles by the Meridian describing the cause of downtime that is attributable to component failures within the production cycles. Four approaches are proposed to address downtime, that included: a new deployment mechanism, which proposed preservation of the current DCMs and implementing a new placement mechanism; multi-layer (sliced-type) Die and a wedge type die retainer that address the development of new type DCMs, to reduce downtime due to deployment and failures; and lastly the inclusion of redundancy or the adoption of new drive technology to reduce downtime due to DCMs failures.

References

Annaz, F. Y. (2014). Design and development of multi-lane smart electromechanical actuators, IET.

Annaz, F. Y. (2016). Online repairable manufacturing robot, European Patent.

Bodanis, D. (2011). E=mc2: a biography of the World's most famous equation, Berkley Group.

Brown R. E. (2008). Future of magnesium developments in 21st Century. Presentation at Materials Science & Technology Conference, Pittsburgh, PA, USA, October 5-9.

Brown, R. E. (2009). Magnesium in the 21st Century. [online] Available at: http://www.asminternational.org/documents/10192/1889138/amp16701p31.pdf/ec559b3f-35f5-4371-8d6c-f490f3f743af, [Accessed 21 June 2017].

Carpenter, J. (2017). Dow Chemical and UFO Debris. [ONLINE] Available at: http://www.nicap.org/reports/ubatubadow2.htm , [Accessed 21 June 2017].

Emley, E. F. (1966). Principles of magnesium technology, Pergamon Press.

Friedrich, H. and Schumann, S. (2001). *Journal of Materials Processing Technology, 117*, 276-281.

Luo, A. (2013). Magnesium casting technology for structural applications, *J. Magnes. Alloys, 1*, 2–22.

Meridian (2017). Meridian, [ONLINE] Available at: http://www.meridian-mag.com/about-meridian/capabilities/ , [Accessed 21 June 2017].

Powell, B., Krajewski P., and Luo A. (2010). Chapter 4: Magnesium Alloys. Book chapter in: Materials Design and Manufacturing for Lightweight Vehicles, Woodhead Publishing Ltd, Cambridge, 114-168.

Schumann, S. and Friedrich, H. (1998). The use of magnesium in cars today and in the future. In:- B. Mordike, K. Kainer (Eds.), Magnesium Alloys and Their Applications, Werkstoff-Informationsgesellschaft, Frankfurt, Germany, pp. 3-13.

Evaluation of a Strut Top Mount for a Magnesium Space Frame Structure for Mainstream Road Cars

Richard H. Cornish

School of Engineering and the Built Environment, Birmingham City University, Millennium Point, Birmingham, B4 7AP, UK.

Email: richard.cornish@bcu.ac.uk

ABSTRACT

The widespread use of magnesium castings in mainstream road vehicles is one way of reducing vehicle mass and hence fuel consumption. The use of magnesium alloys could be encouraged by a gradual improvement in the technical support available. The design limits could be stress based, but with better failure criteria, such as Christensen (2014) proposed. These criteria are more sophisticated than von Mises and could provide a useful addition to the safety margin. In addition, the application of damage models caused by the growth and amalgamation of inclusions, will allow fatigue life and stress corrosion estimates to be refined. As better alloys and alloy systems become available, and the cost per kilogram weight saved increases, there should be enough of a margin to justify the increased design and analysis costs. Finally, vehicle quality and consistency will begin to improve pulling residual values and recycling activity upwards. Casting frames, joints and beams will reduce the structural variability of vehicle body structures. This should enhance vehicle safety, dynamics and refinement, and the proposition of car ownership in future.

Keywords

Material Models, Damage Models, Car Body Structures, Variability, Noise, Vibration and Refinement

INTRODUCTION

Vehicle body durability and consistency is important for vehicle perceived quality. Mainstream vehicles must meet kerb weight limits, including batteries and hybrid power units, so that payload can be added up to the maximum weight. Many of these vehicles are used in towns and cities for short journeys. Light commercial vehicles with a high payload capability were studied extensively to try to understand both the causes and impact of structural variation (Cornish, 1998). These vehicle structures are very lightly damped and exhibit high variability (Rashid *et al.*, 2004). It is expected that the trend towards hybrid and electric propulsion will increase the trend towards lightweight body construction. In addition, Lausecker *et al.* (2017) have found that tests in a Nissan Leaf show that interior road noise around town is much more intrusive than expected, exceeded competitor benchmarks, and probably the high level of interior noise was due to noisy tyres and high tyre pressures. Noisy tyres are a consequence of wanting to achieve low rolling resistance. High tyre pressures are a consequence of carrying a heavy battery pack.

CAR BODY DESIGN CONSIDERATIONS

Mainstream car body design has previously used steel sheet at a gauge of 0.9 to 3.5 mm. The visible panels are cold rolled, around 1 mm in thickness, and have to be highly formed and corrosion treated, with a 'grade A' paint finish. Alternatively, heavier gauges are hot-rolled and are used in frames to provide structural support. Cars also use side frames and floor frames for structural stiffness resisting major bending and torsion loads (Brown, 2003). These frames perform crucial locate and retain functions for the suspension components.

Steel frames provide manufacturing formability, and safe elongation should extreme events occur, both on and off-highway.

It is accepted, but not generally known by the public, that some permanent local deformation of location points, such as strut top mounts, will occur during extreme but predictable events. Repair and adjustments can be picked up at service intervals (wheel misalignment, tracking *etc.*). It is the plastic yielding of steel that gives cars safe levels of reserve strength at low cost (Malen, 2011).

For lightweight vehicles, magnesium material may be a viable proposition in the mid- to long-term. Aluminium has been used successfully by several respected vehicle manufacturers. For example, Tesla has successfully created a brand using extruded aluminium beams and cast joints. Access to Tesla designs has enabled the author to configure a space frame magnesium structure for cars. Design details are given in Tables 1 and 2. To examine this idea further, the space frame concept can be a useful architecture to consider. This chapter will explore one aspect of this structure in magnesium: the critically loaded suspension location casting known as the strut top mounting.

TABLE 1: Overall dimensions for a magnesium space frame vehicle.

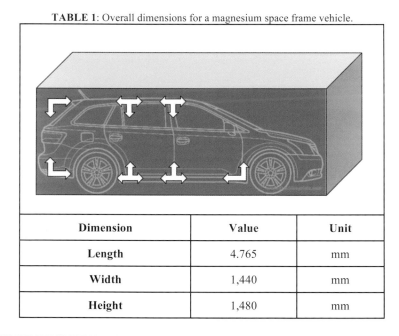

Dimension	Value	Unit
Length	4.765	mm
Width	1,440	mm
Height	1,480	mm

REVIEW OF DESIGN INFORMATION FROM TESLA S-TYPE

The Tesla S-type has a cast aluminium structure and is a very instructive example for the development of a magnesium car body structure. Design details are shown in Figures 1 and 2 with close-up photographs taken by the author. The Tesla S-type has suspension struts mounted to the body shell close to the wheel/road contact points. The design of these mountings are some of the most demanding in terms of peak load and number of cyclic loadings. Mountings are located close to the engine and so must survive in a corrosive environment with high and cyclic levels of mechanical stress and elevated temperatures.

TABLE 2: Design goals for cast joints in the magnesium space frame vehicle.

Joint description	Average joint stiffness	Standard deviation	Unit
A pillar to hinge joint	200 000	+/- 10%	Nm/rad
Hinge pillar to rocker	200 000	+/- 10%	Nm/rad
A pillar to roof side rail	10 000	+/- 10%	Nm/rad
B pillar to roof side rail	10 000	+/- 10%	Nm/rad
B pillar to rocker	200 000	+/- 10%	Nm/rad

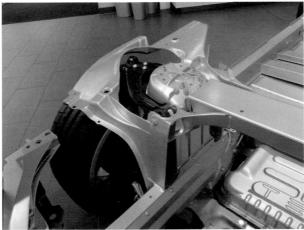

FIGURE 1: The Tesla S-type car body platform in aluminium alloy with close up of the top mounting plate with six pointed star reinforcement bead lines.

FIGURE 2: Side view of the strut top plate in Magnesium alloy, showing the vertical beams beneath each strut top mounting which spread the very considerable vertical loads from the strut top mountings to the extruded chassis rails.

Magnesium has been the subjected to intense research activity to improve its properties through a deeper understanding of its structure. Magnesium alloys with a cubic structure provide castings with a reasonable strength for automotive use. An example is the magnesium radiator support for the Ford F-150 truck. Three consecutive generations of Ford's F-150 full-size truck have been assembled with a die-cast magnesium alloy radiator support. There has been a reduction in mass can at each model change. This was due to improved design, corrosion mitigation, and modular assembly. Alongside such applications, engineers are trying to enhance the ductility of cast and wrought magnesium alloy products. Poor ductility has been a major barrier to widespread applications of cast and wrought magnesium alloys in structural applications.

MATERIAL MODEL OF FAILURE

A deeper understanding of failure criteria may help produce better designs. Studies of the fatigue cracking of AZ91 show that a safe alternating stress is possible of around 25 MPa on top of a mean static stress of 100 MPa. Christensen (2014) has published failure characterisation is based on the physical observation and hypothesis that the general isotropic failure behaviour is completely organised by the T/C value, where T and C are the uniaxial tensile and compressive strengths, Figure 3. This two property failure criterion is quadratic in nature and can predict failure based on the principal stresses. If this directional criterion were applied at the design stage, it could deliver a useful amount of extra safety margin. Figure 3 shows the range of characteristics that can be handled by Christensen's model. For magnesium alloy the tensile stress for failure, T = 75 MPa, compressive stress for failure, C = 160 MPa, and so a ratio of T over C of 75/160 or 0.47.

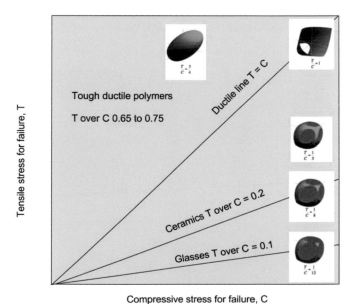

FIGURE 3: Failures surface after Christensen, with coordinate axes principal stress divided by C, where C and T are the failure stresses in pure compression and tension, respectively.

RESULTS

Results shown in Table 3 show that with a pressure of 1 MPa applied to the strut top mounting, the stress in the part was at most 3 MPa. With more reasonable application of pressure over a wider area, the stress in the part was reduced to 0.25 MPa. This fits within the advised limits of safe alternating stress of around 25 MPa on top of a mean static stress of 100 MPa. The author believes that strut top mountings will become feasible in the near future for automotive use.

TABLE 3: Finite element analysis results for the proposed magnesium strut top mount.

Fixation	Pressure applied	Stress
Holes a, b and c	Collar	3.1 MPa
Holes a, b and c and all edge faces	Face	0.25 MPa

DISCUSSION

The application of magnesium will require extensive changes to the way that automotive bodies are designed. However, many of these changes are already being undertaken as aluminium is being applied. The FEA model was linear and subjected to basic load response analysis. This needs to be extended into the nonlinear regime with crack, fatigue and corrosion models, which will be possible with a licence of Abaqus software. The Gurson model of fracture could then be employed, and surface effects modelled with a layer of much harder MgO.

CONCLUSIONS

Development of design and analysis techniques will make it possible to use existing alloys and casting techniques for much more of the car body structure than at present. This will be achieved with larger margins of safety and fatigue and corrosion resistance due to better modelling. As a next step, surface treatments will be developed to extend the fatigue life and resistance to cracking. Finally, as better alloys and processes become available, this trend will only increase.

Acknowledgements
The author would like to thank Meridian for helpful discussions, Tesla UK for access to their vehicles, BCU for use of the Nissan Leaf electric vehicle.

References
Brown, J., Robertson, A. and Serpento, S. (2003). *Motor vehicle structures*. Oxford [u.a.]: Butterworth-Heinemann.
Christensen, R. (2014). *The Theory of Materials Failure*. Oxford: OUP Oxford.
Cornish, R. H. (1998). An investigation of the role of vehicle body variability in interior noise variability of light commercial vehicles. Unpublished PhD Thesis: University of Central England.
Lausecker, D. T. A., Naveen Krishna, Prince Pathania, Anirudh Swaminathan and Richard Cornish (2017). Target setting for interior noise in advanced powertrain vehicles, [pdf]. FPC 2017 Future Powertrain Conference, March 2017, available at https://futurepowertrains.co.uk/, accessed June 2017.
Malen, D. (2011). *Fundamentals of automobile body structure design*. Warrendale, PA: SAE International.
Mariana Kuffova (2011). Fatigue endurance of magnesium alloys, Magnesium Alloys - Design, Processing and Properties, [pdf], Frank Czerwinski (Ed.), ISBN: 978-953-307-520-4, InTech, Available from: http://www.intechopen.com/books/magnesium-alloys-design-processing-and-properties/fatigue-endurance-of-magnesium-alloys, accessed June 2017.
Rashid, R., Langley R. S., Cornish R. H. (2004). Modelling and analysis of in-vehicle boom noise', Proceedings of the Institute of Acoustics, Vol. 26. Pt.2.

A Testbed Platform for UAV Emergency Deployment

Fawaz Y Annaz, Ian Hawkins* and Steve Howard*

¹School of Engineering and the Built Environment, Birmingham City University, Millennium Point, Birmingham, B4 7AP
Email: fawaz.annaz@bcu.ac.uk

²Meridian Lightweight Technologies, Orchard Way, Calladine Park, Sutton-In-Ashfield, Nottinghamshire, NG171JU.
Emails: ihawkins@meridian-mag.com ; showard@meridian-mag.com

Abstract

Despite the safety measures taken by manufacturer, accidents, fires, or even explosions still remain a possible reality. To reduce the likelihood of such events, prevention plays a very important part. Some of these measures include: housekeeping, work habits, workforce training, regular maintenance and inspection/testing of equipment. It is also important to train staff, schedule emergency drills to identify weaknesses, check secondary emergency systems (lighting, pumps, ventilations, *etc.*), and update emergency contacts and any necessary first aid supplies. Industries with die casting facilities need to carry out extra prevention precautions, such as the maintenance of clean and dry site, as well as implementing other process precautions such as planned preheating, cooling and dust control. While prevention measures significantly reduce the damage and recovery time, they should always be accompanied by emergency action plans before, during, and after accidents take place. The presented work fits within the prevention, emergency actions, and the aftermath of accidents. The final goal will be to deploy Unmanned Arial Vehicles (UAVs) within installations such as the Meridian, to search for survivors, and to assess damage, in the event of an accident. To achieve this, the research introduces the new concept of Hardware-Virtual Environment (UAV-VE) Coupling, and presents a testbed platform that allows a UAV to navigate a VE that duplicates real surroundings, such as the Meridian's (or other facilities such as: nuclear reactors, oil rigs, *etc.*). The testbed will be used to map accurate and calibrated UAV manoeuvres onto VEs, and vice versa. In the event of an accident, a trained operator will deploy a UAV to search the facility, through steering the UAV paths within the VE. The UAV will in turn transmit back live pictures and data to assess damage and report the presence of survivors. The approach will help rescue teams in evacuating survivors and also eliminate unnecessary risks to the team. Moreover, this approach can also be used on regular basis to carry out maintenance inspections to areas around the plant that are not easily accessible, for example, roofs, ceiling and ventilation systems.

Keywords
Testbed Platform, Virtual Environment, UAVs

INTRODUCTION

Sir Humphrey Davy is credited for the discovery of Magnesium in 1808, along with other elements such as aluminium, sodium, calcium, barium and strontium (Brown, 2009). Michael Faraday (who became a co-worker following Davy's accident) had many achievements including extracting magnesium using electrolysis in 1833. However, its commercial production by electrolysis is credited to Robert Bunsen in 1952 (Bodanis, 2011).

Magnesium structural applications were mostly limited to Germany before finding its way into the United States, where shortly after World War I, Dow Chemicals developed the alloy 'Dowmetal'. This achievement was followed by the success of the "Idea man", John Josef Grebe (from Dow Chemicals), in devising a method for the extraction of magnesium from seawater, which became the main source of magnesium, as a cubic mile of seawater contains six million tons of magnesium metal (Carpenter, 2017).

The unique properties of magnesium made it very attractive to the automotive industry. It was first used in developing the racing engine pistons for the Indy-500 in 1921 (Luo, 2013) and (Brown, 2008), and was subsequently used in varying degrees within the automotive industry, such as in building pistons (peaked in 1937, with over 4 million of them were in operation) (Brown & Lee, 2012), and in the sandcast crankcase on the 1931 Chevrolair by GM (Powell, Krajewski, & Luo, 2010).

In the United Kingdom, commercial applications of magnesium (in the 1930's) included the development of lower crankcases in city buses and the transmission housings for tractors (Emley, 1966), while in Germany, it was used in making air-cooled engine and gearbox castings in the Volkswagen Beetle. However, in the late 1970's there were demands for producing engines with greater powers that run at higher temperatures, in which water was as engine coolant (Friedrich & Schumann, 2001). This put magnesium at a disadvantage because of its poor corrosion resistance which ultimately resulted in a decline in its use (Schumann & Friedrich, 1998).

Nonetheless, magnesium is making a comeback in vehicle light-weighting, driven by the need to improve fuel economy. Therefore, once again magnesium has become the focus of research and development in many countries around the world in applications such as replacing steel stampings in interior applications; powertrain components; and, limited use in body and chassis components (Luo, 2013).

DIE CASTING TECHNOLOGY AND THE MERIDIAN JOURNEY

Magnesium die casting technologies were long developed during and after World War II due to the economic advantages it offered in mass-production. Recent developments have been focused on the development of thin-wall die casting applications. Injected molten magnesium alloys into the dies result in uniform castings with good surface finish and accurate dimensions with little or no post-machining necessary.

Meridian Lightweight Technologies started magnesium die casting back in 1981 to globally supply clients from the automotive industry in North American, European, and Asia (Technologies, 2017). The process utilises heavy die casting tools and other secondary machining techniques. The manufactured parts are either made from AZ91D, AM60B, or AM50A to achieve the uniquely set properties and performance characteristics that are best suited to specific applications. Typically, AM60B is the most commonly used alloy, due to its excellent ductility, energy absorbing properties, strength and castability.

MAGNESIUM IN THE AUTOMOTIVE INDUSTRY

Safety Challenges
Die casting plants might use combustible metals that could generate combustible metal dust that could cause explosions and fires with catastrophic consequences. The dust deposited on equipment and other surfaces can be transformed, when disturbed, into a cloud that can easily ignite and explode. Such dangers are contained through the use of carefully positioned safety vents and dust collectors, thus it is also crucial to maintain low to none dust deposits around the facility itself (OSHA Safety and Health Information Bulletin, 2005).

Moreover, it has been reported that magnesium fire could burned for hours, resulting in thick white smoke with high heat intensity that vaporises water instantly, splitting it into its atomic constituents, oxygen and hydrogen, with the latter resulting in dramatic explosion in the form of a blinding balls of flame, as shown in Figure 1.

FIGURE 1: Smoke due to magnesium explosion (from a video posted by watchthisusa).

Exercised Precautions by Manufacturers
The Meridian exercises several preventive actions in the manufacturing processes to reduce any associated health and fire hazards. Such measures include enforcing strict housekeeping, workforce training, and conducting regular maintenance, equipment inspection and testing. Moreover, the company schedules regular emergency drills to identify possible weaknesses, check secondary emergency systems and update necessary first aid supplies. Additional precautionary measures include maintenance of clean and dry work sites, as well as magnesium dust control. Although these preventative measures significantly reduce the likelihood of accidents, the company strives towards employing new innovative means to further reduce this possible hazard.

THE PROPOSED PLATFORMS

In view of the hazardous manufacturing environment in die casting plants, there is growing demand to develop test-bed platforms to safely fly Unmanned Aerial Vehicles (UAVs), particularly in the fields of control, monitoring and navigation. Despite the popularity of computer simulations among researchers, their accuracy can be compromised due to hardware modelling approximation. The introduction of the new concept of Hardware-Virtual-Environment (HW-VE) Coupling offer a better alternative to existing conventional methods. The ultimate goal of the new technology is the efficient evaluation, monitoring and control algorithms in randomly created dynamic varying environments without compromising accuracy (Annaz, 2015; Annaz & Khan, 2014; and Khan & Annaz, 2014).

Figure 2 shows the proposed architecture for the HW-VE system, which allows for limited (yet flexible) 3D physical motion mapped (in real-time) onto a 3D VE. The system allows users to observe, record and analyse manoeuvres in various topographies. Designed to support low payload UAVs, it effectively allows unrestricted 3DOF translation along z, rotation movements. Yawing is also sensed by an optical encoder located under the UAV base.

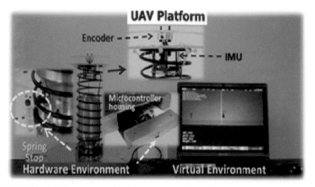

FIGURE 2: The proposed hardware-virtual environment coupling system.

Figure 3 shows a VE example, which was developed using Unity3d to emulate a real-life environment, such as an oil rig or a nuclear plant. The VE has a graphical user interface (GUI) that consists of primary and contextual secondary menus, and implements an auto-hide functionality to free up workspace. The VE was generated using basic objects termed as blocks (which are generated/destroyed via right/left mouse clicking) to create walls, floors and gaps.

FIGURE 3: The dynamic pilot view of a virtual environment.

When the hardware and the VE are properly set up and connected, the detected changes on the testbed are mapped onto the VE. The orientation data is corrected using sensor fusion algorithm to eliminate gyroscopic drift and sensors error accumulation. Once corrected, the data is wirelessly transmitted to the VE, where it will read, parsed, and then mapped onto the virtual VE. This action is repeated on regular intervals, so that the UAV position and orientation is continuously mapped and monitored.

Here, the Meridian die casting facility is proposed as a case study, and a testbed platform will be coupled to a VE that represents the facility. The final goal will be to develop a system that is capable of deploying UAVs to:

- Carry out maintenance inspections to areas around the plant that are not easily accessible, for example, roofs, ceiling and ventilation systems; and
- Deploy UAVs within the installation to search for survivors and to assess damage.

It is proposed that trained operator will deploy and guide a UAV within the facility by steering its paths within the VE. The UAV will in turn transmit back live pictures and data to assess the conditions of inaccessible parts of the plants or report on damage and the presence of survivors, during accidents, thus providing accurate information to evacuate survivors and eliminates unnecessary risks to the team.

CONCLUSION

This chapter provides an introduction to the application of magnesium and die casting in the automotive industry. Clearly, there are some safety challenges that need to be addressed by manufacturers. The use of the newly proposed concept of UAV-VE Coupling, could prove a crucial solution in addressing some of the safety concerns highlighted in this chapter, particularly reducing unnecessary risks taken to rescue and evacuate survivors, as well as carrying out regular maintenance inspections to areas around the plant that are not easily accessible.

References

Annaz, F. (2014). *Design and development of multi-lane smart electromechanical actuators.* IET.

Annaz, F. (2015). UAV testbed training platform development using Panda3d. *Industrials Robot: An International Journal, 42,* (5), 450 - 456.

Annaz, F., & Khan, H. (2014). Hardware-virtual environment integration. Brunei: IET .

Bodanis, D. (2011). *E=mc2: A Biography of the World's Most Famous Equation.* Berkley Publishing Group.

Brown, R. (2008). Future of magnesium developments in 21st Century. Presentation at Materials Science & Technology Conference, Pittsburgh.

Brown, R. (2009). Magnesium in the 21st Century. Retrieved June 21, 2017, from http://www.asminternational.org/documents/10192/1889138/amp16701p31.pdf/ec559b3f-35f5-4371-8d6c-f490f3f743af

Brown, R., & Lee, E. (2012). Magnesium Usage Grew Rapidly in 1930-1950. *Proceedings of 9th International Conference on Magnesium Alloys and Their Applications* (W.J. Poole, K.U. Kainer ed.). Vancouver.

Carpenter, J. (2017). *Dow Chemical and UFO Debris.* Retrieved June 21 2017 from http://www.nicap.org/reports/ubatubadow2.htm

Emley, E. (1966). Principles of Magnesium Technology. Pergamon Press.

Friedrich, H., & Mordike, B. (2006). Magnesium Alloys and Their Applications, *Werkstoff-Informationsgesellschaft* (Mordike, K. Kainer ed.). Springer Science & Business Media.

Friedrich, H., & Schumann, S. (2001). Research for a "new age of magnesium" in the automotive industry. *Journal of Materials Processing Technology, 117,* 276-281.

Khan, H., & Annaz, F. (2014). Using unity for 3D object orientation in a virtual environment. Brunei: IET.

Luo, A. (2013). Magnesium casting technology for structural applications. *J. Magnes. Alloys, 1,* 2–22.

Meridian. (2017). *Meridian.* Retrieved June 21, 2017, from http://www.meridian-mag.com/about-meridian/capabilities/

OSHA Safety and Health Information Bulletin. (2005). *Combustible Dust in Industry: Preventing and Mitigating the Effects of Fire and Explosions.* Retrieved June 21 2017 from http://www.osha.gov/dts/shib/index.html

Powell, B., Krajewski, P., & Luo, A. (2010). Chapter 4: Magnesium Alloys. In *Materials Design and Manufacturing for Lightweight Vehicles* (114-168). Cambridge: Woodhead Publishing Ltd.

Schumann, S., & Friedrich, H. (1998). The use of magnesium in cars today and in the future. In *Magnesium Alloys and Their Applications, Werkstoff-Informationsgesellschaft* (B. Mordike, K. Kainer ed.). Frankfurt.

Technologies, M. L. (2017). *Meridian.* Retrieved June 21, 2017, from http://www.meridian-mag.com/about-meridian/capabilities/

Safety and Energy Assessment on Magnesium-Based Car Parts

Junfeng Yang, Muhammad Arslan and Kieran Jones

School of Engineering and the Built Environment, Birmingham City University, Millennium Point, Birmingham, B4 7AP, UK.
Email: Junfeng.Yang@bcu.ac.uk

Abstract

Magnesium-based car parts have advantages in mechanical properties, *e.g.* lighter, stronger, lower melting point and longer tooling life which benefit vehicle light weighting to further improve energy efficiency and offer low-carbon transport techniques. Thereafter, the application of magnesium component in today's automobile continues to expand. Although magnesium casting technology has been developed successfully to manufacture cars parts, *e.g.* engine block, piston, chassis and transmission housing, very few studies have been conducted to assess the energy efficiency of magnesium casting process and not even preliminary study on the safety performance of these components after vehicle assembly. The objective of present work has two folds: first, investigate the impact of Mg-based material on the vehicle safety, particularly in the vehicle-pedestrian incidents. The human injuries caused by the collision will be assessment for different materials with different vehicle operating conditions; second, assess the application of high pressure die-casting process for manufacturing Mg-based small volume car parts. The energy consumption and processing time of casting processes will be analysed and compared for different die cast metals, *e.g.* steel, Aluminium and magnesium. To achieve this goal, the ANSYS and LS-Dyna Simulation Software have been employed to simulate vehicle-pedestrian collision and the filling and solidification-related casting sub-process respectively. The modelling results suggested that using magnesium improves the energy efficiency of casting process and Mg-based car parts yields the best performance among the available vehicle materials in terms of preventing human injuries during the vehicle-pedestrian collision.

Keywords
Car Parts, Safety, Energy

INTRODUCTION

The high pressure die casting (HPDC) is one of the effective metal forming process characterized by forcing molten metal under high pressure into a mould cavity and wait until it solidifies. A full HPDC process consists of melting, alloying, moulding, pouring, solidification and finishing which are energy intensive manufacturing processes (Campbell, 2004). The typical metal used for die castings are non-ferrous metals, specifically zinc, copper, aluminium, magnesium, lead, pewter and tin-based alloys. Among them, magnesium has many favourable thermophysical properties, *e.g.* low density, low melting point and good mechanical properties. For instance, low heat content favours fast melting and solidification processes. Lower working temperatures extend die life and reduce thermal energy consumption during production. Taking these advantages, the magnesium die cast technique has been widely used to produce the auto parts, *e.g.* powertrain, structural, frame, in the recent decades. To date, a number of research studies have been carried out for identifying opportunities for energy saving for steel and aluminium die cast (Zeng *et al.*, 2014). However, few studies have been reported on the energy consumption of die cast magnesium parts. Therefore, the present work attempts to provide a clear clue on the impact of magnesium material on the energy consumption of die cast manufacturing process.

Moreover, the light weight magnesium auto parts have better dampening capacity and lower inertia that allows vehicle undergoing frequent changes in motion direction (Meridian Lightweight Technologies Inc., 2017) and potentially reduces impact force during the vehicle-vehicle and vehicle-pedestrian collision accident. Since vehicle light weighting technique originally has been developed for the purpose of low energy consumption and carbon emission, few studies attempt to link it with the vehicle safety consideration. Thereafter, it is worth to explore this additional benefit provided magnesium auto parts.

For the above purposes, the high pressure die casting of car parts (*e.g.*, front wind nose of F1 racing car) and vehicle-pedestrian collision have been simulated using Computational Fluid Dynamics (CFD) and Finite Element Analysis (FEA) methods, respectively. The temperature in the mould cavity and the impact force during the collision have been recorded and analysed for different material, *e.g.* steel, aluminium and magnesium under various conditions. The predicted results indicate that magnesium die cast consumes less energy and Mg-based framework yields a better safety performance compared to steel material.

METHODOLOGY

The die casting process involves multiphase (liquid-solid), multiphysics fluid flows with heat and mass transfer. To simulate the die casting process in an accurate manner, the CFD technique together with relevant models, *e.g.* turbulence model, heat transfer model, are essential. During the vehicle-pedestrian collision, the vehicle and human undergo severe momentum exchange and body deformation. The FEA method provides solution for the local strength matrix and integrates it with global matrix, make it more suitable for modelling the collision procedure. Hence, FEA is also adopted in the present work. The governing equations of CFD and FEA have been briefly descried in this section.

Computational Fluid Dynamics

The solidification process during high pressure die casting was treated as a multi-component, multi-phase, heat and mass transfer process, with both the liquid metal phases treated as incompressible immiscible fluids. In the Finite Volume Method framework, the governing equations consist of a continuity equation, Eq. (1) for liquid metal phases, and a single set of momentum and energy equations, Eqs. (2) and (3), respectively:

$$\frac{\partial}{\partial t}(\rho) + \nabla \cdot (\rho \mathbf{u}) = S \qquad \text{Equation [1]}$$

$$\frac{\partial}{\partial t}(\rho \mathbf{u}) + \nabla \cdot (\rho \mathbf{u}\mathbf{u}) = -\nabla p + \nabla \cdot (\mu(\nabla \mathbf{u} + \nabla \mathbf{u}^{\mathsf{T}})) + \rho \mathbf{g} + F_{vol} \qquad \text{Equation [2]}$$

$$\frac{\partial}{\partial t}(\rho h_s) + \nabla \cdot (\mathbf{u}(\rho h_s + p)) = \nabla \cdot \left(\lambda \nabla T - \nabla \cdot \left[\sum_{q=1}^{n} h_{s,q}(\rho D_{m,q} \nabla Y_q) \right] \right) + S_h \qquad \text{Equation [3]}$$

where, ρ and u are the density and velocity of liquid metal, respectively, p and g indicate pressure and gravitational acceleration respectively. Here, $\partial/\partial t$ denotes the partial derivative with respect to time, and ∇ the gradient operator. μ is the viscosity and λ is the thermal conductivity of the fluid. h_s is defined as the sum of species enthalpy, which is based on the specific heat (C_p) of that species and the shared temperature (T).

The enthalpy-porosity technique treats the mushy region (partially solidified region) as a porous medium. The porosity in each cell is set equal to the liquid fraction in that cell. In fully solidified regions, the porosity is equal to zero, which extinguishes the velocities in these regions. The source term, S, on the right-hand-side of momentum equation due to the reduced porosity in the mushy zone takes the following form:

$$S = \frac{(1 - \beta)^2}{(\beta^3 + \epsilon)} A_{mush} \mathbf{u} \qquad \text{Equation [4]}$$

where β is the liquid volume fraction, ϵ is a small number to prevent division by zero, A_{mush} is the mushy zone constant.

Finite Element Analysis

In the FEA method, the time-dependent deformation for which a point initially at X_i ($i = 1, 2, 3$) in a fixed rectangular Cartesian coordinate system moves to a point x_i in the same coordinate system. Since a Lagrangian formulation is considered, the deformation can be expressed in terms of the convected coordinates X_i, and time t. A solution to the momentum equation and mass conservation is written as:

$$\sigma_{ij,j} + \rho f_i = \rho \ddot{x}_i \qquad \text{Equation [5]}$$

$$\rho V = \rho_0 \qquad \text{Equation [6]}$$

where σ is the Cauchy stress, ρ is the current density, $\mathbf{f}$ is the body force density, and $\ddot{x}_i$ is acceleration. V is the V is the relative volume, i.e., the determinant of the deformation gradient matrix, F_{ij},

$$F_{ij} = \frac{\partial x_i}{\partial X_i} \qquad \text{Equation [7]}$$

and ρ_0 is the reference density.

RESULTS AND DISCUSSION

The CFD simulation on die casting of front wind nose and the FEA simulation on vehicle-pedestrian under various conditions have performed based on the ANSYS Fluent (ANSYS FLUENT, 2014) and LS-Dyna (LSTC, 2009) software, respectively. Three different material, *i.e.* carbon steel, aluminium and magnesium have been tested for these simulation for a comparative study.

Die Casting Modelling

A front wind nose plays a key role to stabilize the racing car (see Figure 1 (left)) during fast movement. A 3D unstructured mesh for the mould cavity of front wind nose (see Figure 1 (right)) has been constructed for die cast simulation using ICEMCFD mesh generator (ANSYS ICEMCFD, 2014). The typical auto parts die casting conditions have been adopted for the present boundary setup, *e.g.* inlet velocity and wall temperature. The predicted instantaneous contours of molten metal flowing through the mould cavity are presented in Figure 2. As shown, the molten metal (iso-surface in red colour) gradually filled the whole

78

cavity during the die casting process. The normalized temperature of mould cavity as a function of time has been compared for different die cast metals, *e.g.* steel, aluminium and magnesium, see Figure 3. Once normalized temperature curves are flat plateau, it indicates the die cast metal approaches the equilibrium state during the pouring and solidification processes. As shown, aluminium and magnesium save 62% and 72% of time to reach the equilibrium to complete the solidification process comparing to carbon steel. In addition, the temperature increment representing the total energy consumption indicates aluminium and magnesium reduce the 15% and 20% of total thermal energy consumption compared to carbon steel. This observation is consistent with peer's conclusion that light weight magnesium requires far less energy during the entire die cast production process.

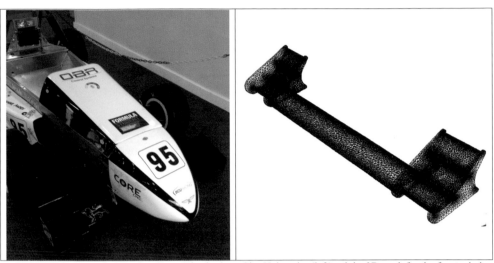

FIGURE 1: Formula 1 Racing Car at Birmingham City University (left)and the 3D mesh for the front wind nose (right).

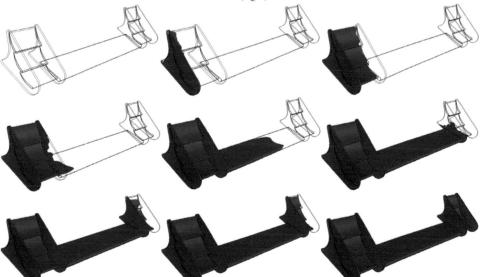

FIGURE 2: Predicted instantaneous contour of molten metal flowing through a mold cavity of front wind nose during the high pressure die casting process. The molten magnesium is in red colour.

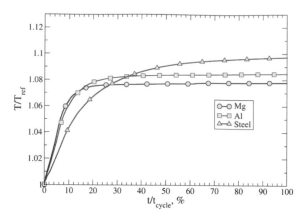

FIGURE 3: Predicted averaged temperature inside the mold cavity as a function of time for die casting process.

Vehicle-Pedestrian Modelling

Regarding the vehicle-pedestrian simulation, the FE models for a commercial passenger car model and an adult model have been constructed based on the LS-Dyna platform. The preliminary test employs a conventional carbon steel frame moving toward a static adult. The snapshots showing the vehicle-pedestrian collision consequence were given in Figure 4 (left). Since the impact force directly determines the severity of human injuries, the impact force distribution in human body and vehicle frame were illustrated in Figure 4 (right). One can see that the impact force first develops in lower abdomen area and then spreads to rest of the body. However, it reaches its maximum value in lower approximates of the human body and upper knees areas. Hence, there are fewer chances to develop head injuries in this collision. Also notice the maximum impact force developed in vehicle frame remained in its central part of body so if we install an impact absorbent material in that area, more potential injuries can be avoided. These contours help recognize the most effected region qualitatively. To obtain quantitative analysis results, the impact forces are plotted as a function of time for vehicle-pedestrian collision with a range of 30-50 mph, see Figure 5.

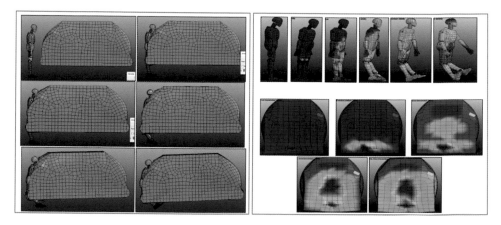

FIGURE 4: Snapshots showing the vehicle-pedestrian collision procedure (left). Impact force distribution in pedestrian and vehicle front (right). Note: All stresses resulted for collision in x-direction only.

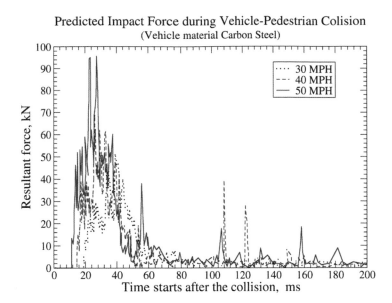

Predicted Impact Force during Vehicle-Pedestrian Colision
(Vehicle material Carbon Steel)

FIGURE 5: Predicted impact force as a function of time as the consequence of vehicle-pedestrian collision with a carbon steel frame vehicle at the speed range of 30-50MPH.

It is clear from the plots that higher vehicle speed will result higher impact force, thus more severe injuries. Peak force increases from 50 kN to 100kN as the vehicle speeding up from 30 mph to 50 mph. Reason behind this phenomenon is momentum. Higher the speed for same mass means higher the momentum as given by $M = mv$, where M for momentum, m for mass and v for velocity. As a result, we can limit the vehicle operational speed to less than 30 mph, especially if it is used in airport, theme parks, industrial facility so many but few. One other thing to notice is, the time to reach maximum force, which is roughly 38 ms for slower speed and 26 ms for higher speed. That means a faster deceleration culminating in sudden variation of forces in human body. The last notable feature of higher speed is 'aftershocks'. It is clear from Figure 5 that the human body experiences secondary peak forces, after 100ms, so constituting further possible injuries.

The predicted impact forces as a function of time for different materials (steel, Al and Mg) have been compared under the collision speeds 30 mph and 40 mph, see Figure 6. For carbon steel, it can be seen the peak force developed in pedestrian body is very high and it has also multiple peaks, indicating multiple impacts between pod and pedestrian. This trend is similar to aluminium frame, but not for Mg frame. Though the built up peak force is least for aluminium frame pod. By considering area under the graph, we can determine impulse of the human body, under investigation, and it is least for collision with magnesium frame. Area under the graph equals to impulse, defined as $\Delta p = F \Delta t$, meaning there is less change in momentum in pedestrian body during the impact, ultimately resulting in less development of collision forces.

In addition, observe the gradient of these graphs and which is least steep for the magnesium frame. This clearly states that rate of forces developed in pedestrian body, is gradual or the jerk $(=\Delta a/\Delta t)$ developed is lowest for pedestrian-Mg frame collision. Otherwise, a body will keep applying different amounts of forces in different direction to counter jerk.

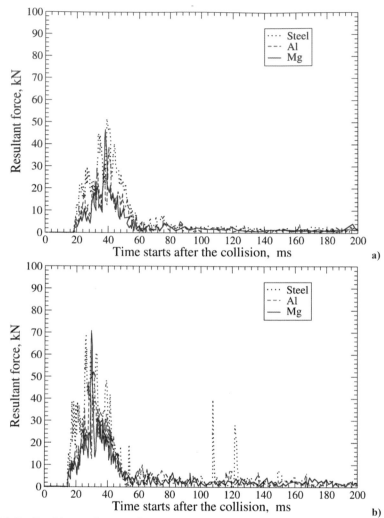

FIGURE 6: Predicted impact force as a function of time for different materials under collision speeds: a) 30 mph; and b) 40 mph.

CONCLUSION

The present work investigated the impact of light-weighting material, magnesium, on the energy consumption of die-casting process and the vehicle crash safety. For these purposes, the die cast process of front wind nose and the vehicle-pedestrian collision has been simulated using CFD and FEA methods. The modelling results indicate that using magnesium reduces 72% of time and 20% energy consumption for the die casting process compared to carbon steel. In addition, the vehicle frame made from magnesium tends to produce the lowest average impact forces to the human body during the vehicle-pedestrian collision, which represents the lowest level of injury severity.

In terms of future work, we would like to continue magnesium die-casting simulation to obtain in-depth understanding on the energy consumption in each sub-process and identify the energy saving potential for die-casting industries. In addition, the deformation of Mg-based auto parts during the accident needs to be investigated further.

Acknowledgements
Mr. Hunny Mahal is acknowledged for sharing the CFD mesh for the die casting modelling.

References
ANSYS®Academic Research, Release 15.0, Help System, "ANSYS ICEMCFD Manual," ANSYS, Inc., 2014.
ANSYS®Academic Research, Release 15.0, Help System, "ANSYS FLUENT Manual," ANSYS, Inc., 2014.
Campbell, J. and Richard, A. (1994). Solidification defects in castings, European Aluminum Association (EEA).
LSTC. "LS-DYNA Keyword User's Manual, Volume 1" (PDF). Livermore Software Technology Corporation (LSTC). Retrieved 2009-03-25.
Meridian Lightweight Technologies Inc. www.meridian-mag.com/
Zeng, B., Jolly, M., Salonitis, K. (2014). Manufacturing cost modelling of castings produced with CRIMSON process. TMS Annual Meeting, 201-208

An Assessment of Lightweight Vehicles to Reduce Greenhouse Gas Emissions with Focus on Magnesium

Siddharth Suhas Kulkarni and José Ricardo Sodré*

School of Engineering and the Built Environment, Birmingham City University, Millennium Point, Birmingham, B4 7XG, UK.
Email: siddharth.kulkarni@bcu.ac.uk; ricardo.sodre@bcu.ac.uk

Abstract

As a result of tougher regulatory requirements to control greenhouse gas emissions, vehicle weight reduction appears as one of the alternatives. In view of this, the use of lightweight materials to replace conventional steel in passenger vehicles with internal combustion engines has gained permanent attention. This work assesses the potential of replacing to automotive steel components by light metals, with a focus on magnesium, to achieve mass reduction and, consequently, reduced fuel consumption and greenhouse gas emissions. Magnesium is the eight most abundant element available on Earth and composes about 2% of Earth's crust by weight. The very low density of magnesium makes it very suitable for light weighting, as it is also a third lighter than aluminium, and three-quarters lighter than steel. The corrosion resistance is also higher than traditional aluminium. Cast magnesium also solidifies faster due to lower latent heat, hence more castings can be produced than aluminium at one given time. The opportunities for innovation in alloying, processing and integration of magnesium to automotive applications are, therefore, overviewed.

Keywords
Lightweight Materials, Emission Reduction, Greenhouse Gas Emissions

INTRODUCTION

In the recent years, road passenger transportation faced a global challenge in terms of reducing environmental pollution and greenhouse gas emissions (GHG) (Palencia *et al.*, 2012; Lewis *et al.*, 2014). The US, Europe, other countries and regions have introduced many regulations on the sales and development of passenger vehicles to reduce vehicle mass and, consequently, carbon dioxide (CO_2) emissions (Kim *et al.*, 2010; Elgowaingy *et al.*, 2010). Thus, lightweight materials gained popularity for passenger transportation vehicle development, to reduce fuel consumption and the formation of exhaust emissions. Traditionally, internal combustion engines (ICE) have been used for propulsion of passenger vehicles, fuelled with fossil and alternative fuels that produce different levels of CO_2 emissions. Automotive weight reduction can be achieved either by component downsizing or materials substitution, the latter being the subject of this review. Conventional steel has higher density than lightweight materials, but must still be used depending on the vehicle part and application (Ou *et al.*, 2012; Jimenez-Espadafor *et al.*, 2011). In recent years, vehicle weight has been increased due to safety requirements and luxury intent with awkward effects on energy efficiency and CO_2 emissions (Patton *et al.*, 2004).

Du *et al.* (2010) studied the impact of increasing the content of aluminium on the Chinese automobile fleet between 2010 and 2020. Combining a lifecycle assessment methodology to estimate the energy use and CO_2 emissions during the vehicle life, a vehicle fleet model was developed to estimate energy consumption, greenhouse gas (GHG) emissions and aluminium

---

* Author to whom any correspondence should be addressed.

requirements from the vehicle fleet. However, only ICE vehicles and aluminium as lightweight material were considered. Also for China, Hao et al. (2011) studied the effect of constraining vehicle registration, reducing vehicle travel, strengthening fuel consumption limits, vehicle downsizing and BEV (Battery Electric Vehicle) penetration on passenger vehicle fleet energy consumption and GHG emissions between 2010 and 2050 without assessing the vehicle fleet cost. For Colombia, Palencia et al. (2014) studied the effect of powertrain electrification and lightweight materials use on passenger car fleet energy use, materials use, CO_2 emissions and cost without considering downsizing. In the context of developed countries, Bandivadekar et al. (2008) assessed the potential of powertrain electrification, lightweight materials substitution and vehicle size reduction for energy consumption and CO_2 emissions reduction.

As mentioned before, a way to reduce automotive fuel consumption and, consequently, CO_2 emissions is the application of light weighting. An investigation conducted on 2010-2014 vehicle models in China concluded that 18 kg mass reduction improved fuel consumption by 0.07 L/100 km (Hao et al., 2016). For this purpose, magnesium is an adequate light weighting material for vehicles, as it is 33% lighter than aluminium and 75% lighter than steel or cast-iron components (Wenlong et al., 2016). The corrosion resistance of high-purity magnesium alloys is better than conventional aluminium die cast alloys. Magnesium alloys have distinct advantages over aluminium and ferrous materials by virtue of better manufacturability. Compared to aluminium, magnesium solidification is faster due to lower latent heat, thus producing approximately 25-50% more castings per unit time. A lifecycle assessment of a magnesium-built engine block showed its advantageous environmental performance in comparison with functionally equivalent blocks made from aluminium, conventional cast iron and compacted graphite iron (Tharumarajah and Koulton, 2007). The replacement of an engine cylinder block, front cover and oil pan from conventional materials by die casting magnesium AZ91 caused a reduction of 7% on total engine weight (Dhingra and Das, 2014).

Many engineers have studied specialized alloys to reduce vehicle weight, but, traditionally, aluminium and cast iron have been used. This chapter focuses on the assessment and impact of using lightweight materials to reduce vehicle weight, thus reducing CO_2 emissions from transportation vehicles. The next section highlights the current best-practice technologies in manufacturing automobiles using steel, aluminium, and magnesium, followed by a short review on the effects of light weighting on fuel consumption and emissions. Then, the specific use of magnesium on passenger vehicle transportation is briefly reported before some conclusions are achieved.

ASSESSMENT OF LIGHTWEIGHT MATERIALS

The largest possibility to reduce vehicle weight comes from the body structure, and further weight reduction can be achieved by downsizing other components such as the engine (Shi et al., 2007). Traditionally, high strength steel has been used to develop auto-body parts for vehicles, as they have higher yield strength and failure strength than mild steel (Li et al., 2003). Using high steel as a sheet in any automobile body part increases the absorbing energy of the component and also increases its resistance to plastic deformation (Klassen et al., 1998). High strength steel has low fabrication costs and cheaper raw material than aluminium and magnesium (Fridlyander et al., 2002). In the recent years, car makers prefer using aluminium to attend fuel economy and light weighting legislations, despite its high cost. Schbert et al. (2001) devised a total distribution costs for typical car structures made from steel, aluminium, magnesium, and titanium, as demonstrated in Figure 1.

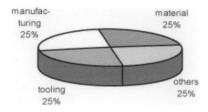

FIGURE 1: Typical cost distribution for car structures (Schbert *et al.*, 2001).

The authors concluded that the total acceptable costs of a new component with new material mainly relies on the tooling and manufacturing costs. Kelkar *et al.* (2001) further analysed the cost of fabrication of aluminium panels as a substitution for steel to meet the regulatory pressures, and concluded that the obstacles to substitute aluminium with steel is the high costs of primary aluminium. The authors also recommended that partial substitution of aluminium by steel would provide better corrosion resistance than steel alone. The body in white (BIW) accounts for about 28% of the entire car weight, as demonstrated by Figure 2.

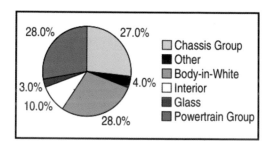

FIGURE 2: Mass distribution in a passenger car (Kelkar *et al.*, 2001).

Ungureanu *et al.*, (2007) developed a sustainability model to quantify the total costs of a vehicle throughout its lifecycle. The authors also presented a quantitative comparison of aluminium and steel alloys to give the details of the economic and environmental performance of a vehicle. The comparative analysis demonstrated by the authors shows that, by using the traditional steel, the vehicle BIW structure is very economical and, as the vehicle usage increases, the materials and use costs increase as compared to using aluminium. The total cost comparison of using aluminium against steel is demonstrated in Figure 3.

Magnesium is the eighth most available element on Earth and also composes about 2% of Earth's crust by weight (Macwan and Chen, 2016). The corrosion resistance is also higher than traditional aluminium cast alloys (Joost and Krajewski, 2017). Magnesium also solidifies faster due to lower latent heat, hence more castings can be produced than aluminium at a given time (Zhao *et al.*, 2008; Fechner *et al.*, 2013). Magnesium was formerly used by Volkswagen Group for their Beetle car, in the air-cooling engine house transmission (Cole, 2003). General Motors used magnesium in the cross-car beams or instrument panels on the 2012 Cadillac SLS with their quick plastic forming (QPF) technology. The QPF technology consisted of blowing hot forming to make high value automotive components (Taub *et al.*, 2007).

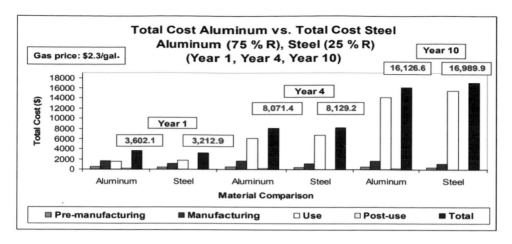

FIGURE 3: Aluminium versus Steel - total cost break down in all the life cycles of a vehicle
(Ungureanu *et al.*, 2007).

LIGHTWEIGHTING EFFECTS ON FUEL CONSUMPTION AND EMISSIONS

Fuel consumption of a passenger transportation vehicle heavily relies on vehicle weight (Koffler and Rohde-Brandenburger, 2009). The representatives of the New European Driving Cycle (NEDC) published a 'real' fuel consumption of passenger cars in Europe in 2004, as demonstrated in Figure 4 (European Union, 2004). Although one can question the accuracy of this data, it provides the constitutional advantage of providing a basic context and approved means of calculating fuel consumption on all driving cycles.

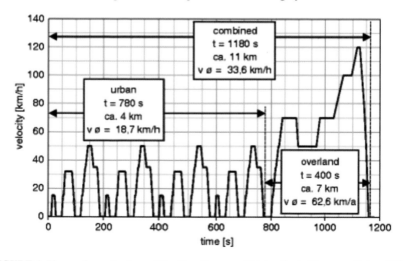

FIGURE 4: Time and speed pattern of the New European Driving Cycle (European Union, 2004).

Ding *et al.* (2015) conducted a sensitivity analysis study to show different energy savings on automobile parts in China by replacing them by aluminium. As an example, their results showed over a vehicle life cycle of 200,000 km driving that, when the typical steel parts were replaced with aluminium parts, the vehicle consumed 1,447 to 1,590 litres less gasoline than it would have with steel parts used. A tailored model to assess the environmental benefits by light weighting on diesel turbocharged vehicles was presented by Delogu *et al.* (2016) based upon Fuel Reduction Value (FRV). Their results showed the FRV was within the range of 0.115–0.143 and 0.142–0.388 L/100 km × 100 kg, respectively, for mass reduction only and powertrain adaptation purposes. Del Pero *et al.* (2016) performed a life-cycle assessment of 2015 European market vehicle case studies to allow a method to estimate fuel consumption reduction by means of FRV. The authors concluded that the method should be extended to the mass induced energy consumption modelling to electric and hybrid vehicles to highlight the benefits of light weighting in the passenger car vehicles sector. Further development of light weighting materials shows the substitution of glass fibers by natural cellulose and kenaf for automobile components (Boland *et al.*, 2015). Though the use of natural cellulose, the life cycle greenhouse gas emissions were reduced by 18.6% with powertrain resizing, and 7.2% without it. By using kenaf composite component, fuel energy consumption was reduced by 6.0%.

Ehsani *et al.* (2016) proposed a new mechanical model for fuel consumption and CO_2 for passenger car vehicles, and investigated three types of tolling parameters such as temperature, asphalt efficiency and fuel efficiency. Based on the boundary conditions of vehicle speed and use of different fuels, a comparison of fuel consumption and CO_2 emissions for different vehicles is demonstrated in Figure 5.

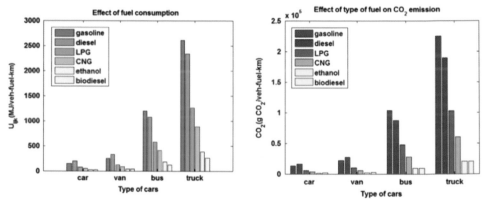

FIGURE 5: Comparison of fuel consumption and CO_2 emissions for different vehicles (Ehsani *et al.*, 2016).

MAGNESIUM APPLICATION

As highlighted in the previous sections, light weight of the automotive structure plays an important part in improving fuel efficiency and reducing CO_2 emissions for a car. At present, magnesium is implemented in the die casting process and is a key technology to replace the traditional steel materials. Park and Kwon (2015) welded magnesium alloy to investigate the dashboard panel die (Figure 6) to be applied for the warm die technology of automotive cars. The thermal simulation performed proved that the temperature distribution could be controlled uniformly.

Koulton *et al.* (2005), through their life cycle assessment, performed a sensitivity analysis of a convertor housing using magnesium in the die-casting, trimming and finishing processes. Their study demonstrated that the total greenhouse gas emissions over the magnesium components achieves significant mass reduction by using the Australian magnesium over standard US aluminium (Figure 7).

FIGURE 6: Ruptured product of the dash panel (Park and Kwon, 2015).

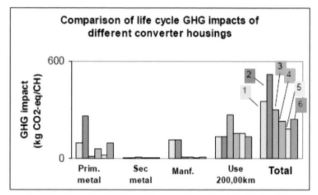

1 – Nominal; 2 – Chinese Mg; 3 – Iron; 4 – AU Al; 5 – US
Al; 6 – AU Mg and AM-cover

FIGURE 7: Greenhouse gas comparisons on different material product systems (after Koulton *et al.*, 2005).

Kiani *et al.* (2014) conducted a structural optimization on the 1996 Dodge Neon car model, to develop a lightweight car design. The authors replaced 22 steel parts with magnesium AZ31 and the design optimization resulted in saving 46.7 kg of overall weight and an approximate mass reduction of 44.3%, when compared to the initial steel design. Thus, by combining the above examples, magnesium offers a superior prospective as a lightweight materials.

CONCLUSION

Automotive materials play an important part in vehicle performance and fuel consumption. This assessment concludes that car body light weighting can significantly improve fuel efficiency and, thus, reduce CO_2 emissions. Due to the tougher EU legislations being introduced on reducing CO_2 emissions, automotive manufacturers are increasingly applying light weight as a technological solution to obtain the desirable improvements. Vehicle mass reduction can be obtained through downsizing, but also through substitution of the traditional automotive materials by lightweight materials, such as magnesium. A few works have been referenced to show how lightweight materials can, in effect, replace traditional steel. Although aluminium alloy application has gained prominence, magnesium proves to be a promising contender to meet future demands of passenger vehicles.

References

Bandivadekar, A., Bodek, K., Cheah, L., Evans, C., Groode, T., Heywood J, *et al.* (2008). On the road in 2035: reducing transportation's petroleum consumption and GHG emissions. Cambridge, Mass.: Massachusetts Institute of Technology.

Boland, S., De Kleine, R., Keoleian, G., Lee, E., Kim, H. and Wallington, T. (2016). Life cycle impacts of natural fiber composites for automotive applications: effects of renewable energy content and lightweighting. *Journal of Industrial Ecology*, 20, 179–189.

Cole, G. D. (2003). Lightweight strategies. Chemical & Engineering News, American Chemical Society, http://pubs.acs.org/cen/80th/magnesium.html, Date Accessed: 10/07/17.

Del Pero F., Delogu, M. and Pierini, M. (2017). The effect of lightweighting in automotive LCA perspective: estimation of mass-induced fuel consumption reduction for gasoline turbocharged vehicles. *Journal of Cleaner Production*, 154, 566-577.

Delogu, M., Del Pero, F. and Pierini, M. (2016). Lightweight design solutions in the automotive field: environmental modelling based on fuel reduction value applied to diesel turbocharged vehicles. *Sustainability*, 8, [11], 1167.

Dhingra, R. and Das, S. (2014). Life cycle energy and environmental evaluation of downsized vs. lightweight material automotive engines. *Journal of Cleaner Production*, 85, 347-358.

Ding, N., Gao, F., Wang, Z. and Yang, J. (2016). Life cycle energy and greenhouse gas emissions of automobiles using aluminium in China. *Journal of Industrial Ecology*, 20, 818–827.

Du, J. D., Han, W. J., Peng, Y. H. and Gu, C. C. (2010). Potential for reducing GHG emissions and energy consumption from implementing the aluminum intensive vehicle fleet in China. *Energy*, 35, [12], 4671 - 4678.

Ehsani, M., Ahmadi, A. and Fadai, D. (2016). Modeling of vehicle fuel consumption and carbon dioxide emission in road transport. *Renewable and Sustainable Energy Reviews*, 53, 1638-1648.

Elgowainy, A., Han, J., Poch, L., Wang, A., Mahalik, M., Rousseau, A. (2010). Well-to-wheels analysis of energy use and greenhouse gas emissions of plug-in hybrid electric vehicles. Argonne National Laboratory

European Union (2004). Directive 2004/3/EC of the European Parliament and of the Council of 11 February 2004 amending Council Directives 70/156/EEC and 80/1268/EEC as regards the measurement of carbon dioxide emissions and fuel consumption of N1 vehicles.

Fechner, D., Blawert, C., Norbert Hort, N., Dieringa, H. and Kainer, K. (2013). Development of a magnesium secondary alloy system for mixed magnesium post-consumer scrap. *Materials Science and Engineering*, 576, 222-230.

Fridlyander, I., Sister, V., Grushko, O., Berstenev, B., Sheveleva, L. and Ivanova, L. (2002). Aluminum alloys: promising materials in the automotive industry. *Metal Science and Heat Treatment*, 3-9.

Gonzalez-Palencia, J., Furubayashi, T. and Nakata, T. (2014). Techno-economic assessment of lightweight and zero emission vehicles deployment in the passenger car fleet of developing countries. *Applied Energy*, 123, 129 -142.

Hao, H., Wang, H. and Ouyang, M. (2011). Fuel conservation and GHG (Greenhouse gas) emissions mitigation scenarios for China's passenger vehicle fleet. *Energy*, 36, [11], 6520 – 6528.

Hao, H., Wang, S., Liu, Z. and Zhao F. (2016). The impact of stepped fuel economy targets on automaker's light-weighting strategy: the China case. *Energy*, 94, 755-765.

Jimenez-Espadafor, F. J., Marı́n, J. J. R., Becerra, J., Garcıa, M. T., Trujillo, E. C. and Ojeda, F. J. F. (2011). Infantry mobility hybrid electric vehicle performance analysis and design. *Applied Energy*, 88, [8], 2641– 2652.

Kim, H., McMillan, C., Keoleian, G. and Skerlos, S. (2010). Greenhouse gas emissions payback for lightweighted vehicles using aluminum and high-strength steel. *Journal of Industrial Ecology*, 14, [6], 929 - 946.

Klassen, M., Skupin, J., Schubert, E. and Sepold, G. (1998). Development of seam imperfections due to process immanent resonances by laser beam welding of aluminium alloys. In:- Proceedings of the Conference on EKLAT'98, Hanover, Germany, September 22–23, 297–302.

Koffler, C. and Rohde-Brandenburger, K. (2009). On the calculation of fuel savings through lightweight design in automotive life cycle assessments. *The International Journal of Life Cycle Assessment*, 15, 128.

Koulton, P., Tharumarajah, A., Ramakrishnan, S. (2005). Life cycle environmental impact of magnesium automotive components. *TMS (The Minerals, Metals & Materials Society)*.

Lewis, A., Kelly, J., Keoleian, G. (2014). Vehicle light weighting vs. electrification: Life cycle energy and GHG

Li, Y., Lin, Z., Jiang, A., Chen G. (2003). Use of high strength steel sheet for lightweight and crashworthy car body. *Materials & Design*, 24, [3], 177-182.

Macwan, A. and Chen D., (2016). Ultrasonic spot welding of rare-earth containing ZEK100 magnesium alloy to 5754 aluminum alloy, *Materials Science and Engineering*, 666, 139-148.

90

Morteza Kiani, Imtiaz Gandikota, Masoud Rais-Rohani, Keiichi Motoyama, Design of lightweight magnesium car body structure under crash and vibration constraints, *Journal of Magnesium and Alloys*, 2, [2], 99-108.

Ou, X., Yan, X., Zhang, X., Liu, Z. (2012) Life-cycle analysis on energy consumption on GHG emission intensities of alternative vehicle fuels in China. *Applied Energy,* 90, [1], 218–224.

Palencia, J., Furubayashi, T., Nakata, T. (2012). Energy use and CO2 emissions reduction potential in passenger car fleet using zero emission vehicles and lightweight materials. *Energy*, 48, [1], 548 – 565.

Park D., Kwon H. (2015) Development of Warm Forming Parts for Automotive Body Dash Panel Using AZ31B Magnesium Alloy Sheets. *International Journal of Precision Engineering and Manufacturing*, 16, 2159 – 2165

Patton, R., Li, F., Edwards, M. (2004) Causes of weight reduction effects of material substitution on constant stiffness components. *Thin-Wall Structures*, 42, [4] 613–637.

Saboohi, Y., Farzaneh, H. (2009) Model for developing an eco-driving strategy of a passenger vehicle based on the least fuel consumption. *Applied Energy*, 86, [10], 1925–1932.

Schubert, E., Klassen, M., Zerner, I., Walz, C., Sepold, G. (2001) Light-weight structures produced by laser beam joining for future applications in automobile and aerospace industry, *Journal of Materials Processing Technology*, 115, [1], 2-8.

Shi, Y., Zhu, P., Shen, L., Lin, Z. (2007) Lightweight design of automotive front side rails with TWB concept, *Thin-Walled Structures*, 45, [1], 8-14.

Taub A., Krajewski P., Luo A., Owens J. (2007) The evolution of technology for materials processing over the last 50 years: The automotive example. *The Journal of The Minerals, Metals & Materials Society (TMS)*, 59, [2], 48–57.

Tharumarajah, A., Koltun, P. (2007) Is there an environmental advantage of using magnesium components for light-weighting cars? *Journal of Cleaner Production*, 15, [11 – 12], 1007-1013.

Ungureanu, C., Das, S., Jawahir, I. (2007) Life-cycle cost analysis: aluminum versus steel in passenger cars. *TMS (The Minerals, Metals & Materials Society)*, 11-24.

Wenlong, S., Xiaokai, C., Lu, W. (2016) Analysis of energy saving and emission reduction of vehicles using lightweight materials, *Energy Procedia*, 88, 889-893.

William J., Joost, P., Krajewski, E. (2017) Towards magnesium alloys for high-volume automotive applications, *Scripta Materialia*, 128, 107-112.

Zhao, M., Liu, M., Song, G., Andrej A., (2008) Influence of the β-phase morphology on the corrosion of the Mg alloy AZ91, *Corrosion Science*, 50, [7], 1939-1953.

Final Thoughts: Reflection & Conclusion

Makhan Singh and Martyn Alderman*

Birmingham City University, 15 Bartholomew Row, Birmingham B5 5JU, UK.
Email: makhan.singh@bcu.ac.uk

*International Magnesium Association, European Committee Chairman
Email: martyn.alderman@magnesium-elektron.com

This book represents a project outcome from an exclusive partnership between Birmingham City University and Meridian Lightweight Technologies UK – the world's largest producer of magnesium die cast components. Since forming in 2016, and a group visit to the factory, the strategic alliance has seen the two organisations work together in the education, research and development of magnesium use, having placed fuel efficiency through weight savings and sustainability within its core.

Further, the partnership, also builds on the heritage of Birmingham City University as a catapult for growth among regional industries through both knowledge transfer and by offering a unique, interdisciplinary approach. At its highest level, it seeks to identify new ways to offer more sustainable goods for low-volume manufacturers whilst making production financially viable for Meridian Lightweight Technologies UK and its potential clients. Through this activity, the partnership looks to transform the fortunes of magnesium, by showcasing it as a viable alternative for the manufacturing sector, including the automotive and the aerospace industry. The strength of the project lies in its levels of collaboration and partnership which spans both academic and professional staff, and the undergraduate and post-graduate student body of Birmingham City University.

From a strategic perspective, the project aligns with Birmingham City University's institutional commitment to STEAM-based learning (STEM with Arts-based subjects). STEAM is designed to drive an increasingly enterprise-focussed education, developing employability and entrepreneurship skills. The challenges set by Meridian Lightweight Technologies clearly demonstrate how arts and creativity can be combined with STEAM subjects to drive innovation, skills, research and economic growth and facilitate innovative solutions to new business ideas, products and services.

On the 20th July 2017, a 'Magnesium Symposium' was held at Birmingham City University in partnership with Meridian Lightweight Technologies. Its purpose was to explore the importance of magnesium within the manufacturing sector – showcasing it as an alternative material, especially for car manufacturers and the aerospace industry in terms of light weighting, fuel efficiency and the circular economy. External partners, such as High Speed Sustainable Manufacturing Institute (HSSMI), International Magnesium Association (IMA) and Forum for the Future, were invited as guest speakers to share their insights. Debate and discussion was further underpinned through presentations from three Birmingham City University academics engaged in the project - Alan Pendry, Dr Panagiotis Rentzelas and Professor Michal Krzyzanowski. Themes discussed at the Symposium included a range of topics such as why magnesium should be used for the next generation of vehicles and aircraft and how safe magnesium is as we dispel the myths around its burning reputation.

Further underlining the principle of partnerships of mutual value, it was stated at the Symposium that Meridian Lightweight Technologies has allocated investment at Birmingham

City University to directly support the promotion of female participation in STEM careers. In the first instance, this will take place through awarding bursaries and work experience to three female students at Birmingham City University. Further, the Plant Manager of Meridian Lightweight Technologies UK has agreed to join a newly established School of Engineering and the Built Environment Industrial Advisory Board at Birmingham City University to promote and maintain strong links with industry and industrial practice; whilst Meridian Lightweight Technologies UK staff have also been invited to support learning through adopting a guest lecturer role. This latter point represents a welcome enhancement to our teaching and learning, and will serve to capture creative and innovative practice that can be shared across the Institution.

Finally, as well as benefiting Meridian Lightweight Technologies UK work here in the Midlands, Birmingham City University anticipates that the findings will enhance lightweight technologies around the world, ensuring that low-volume manufacturers in the automobile and aerospace industries have access to cost-effective and sustainable magnesium components.

FIGURE 1: Birmingham City University and The High Speed Sustainable Manufacturing Institute (HSSMI) visit to Meridian Lightweight Technologies UK for the official launch of the project in January 2017.

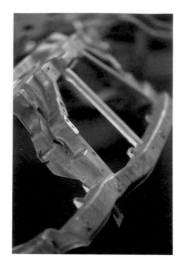

FIGURE 2: Magnesium die cast component produced by Meridian Lightweight Technologies, UK.

FIGURE 3: Delegates who attended the 2017 Magnesium Symposium at Birmingham City University, 20th July 2017.

FIGURE 4: Academics from BCU showcase and discuss their Magnesium posters with delegates.

FIGURE 5: Meridian Lightweight Technologies discuss the partnership benefits with BCU.

Author Index

A

Alaswad, A. 50
Alderman, M. 17
Annaz, F. Y. 82
Annaz, F. Y. 69
Arslan, M. 87

B

Brown, S. 14

C

Chadwick, E. 26
Connor, E. 26
Cornish, R. H. 76

H

Hawkins, I. 69, 82
Howard, S. 69, 82

J

Jones, K. 87

K

Krzyzanowski, M. 55
Krzyztof, M. 55
Kulkarni, S. S. 95

L

Leyland, L. 33

M

Majta, J. 55
Mavritsaki, E. 38

P

Pendry, A. 64

R

Randman, D. 55
Rentzelas, P. 38
Rose, R. 45

S

Shaw, C. 41
Singh, M. 26, 103
Slezak, M. 55
Sodre, J. R. 95

V

Virk, A. 26

Y

Yang, J. 87

Subject Index (by Keywords)

A

Aluminium 14
Attitudes 38

B

Bursary 33

C

Car Body Structures 76
Car Parts 87
Circular Economy 45
Collaboration 41
Crashworthiness 50
Curriculum Innovation 26

D

Damage Models 76
Decarbonisation 45
Die-Casting 69
Downtime 69
Downtime Reduction 64
Dynamic Material Modelling 55

E

Emission Reduction 95
Emotional Intelligence 26
End of Life 17
Energy 87
Energy Absorption 50

F

Formability of Mg-alloys 55

G

Greenhouse Gas Emissions 95

I

Impact 50
Innovation 41

L

Lean Manufacture 64
Life Cycle 17

Lightweight 50
Lightweight Materials 95

M

Magnesium 14
Markets 17
Material Models 76
Mobility 45

N

Noise 76

R

Rheological Testing 55
Robotics 69

S

Safety 87
Sever Plastic Deformation 55
Simulation 55
Single Minute Exchange of Dies 64
SMED 64
Soft Skills 26
Strength 14

T

Technology Adaptation 38
Testbed Platform 82
Theory of Planned Behaviour 38
Theory of Reasoned Action 38

U

UAVs 82

V

Variability 76
Vibration and Refinement 76
Virtual Environment 82
Vulnerability 41

W

WISE 33
Women 33

NOTES